An Introduction to
Engineering Heat Transfer

John R. Simonson

Senior Lecturer in Applied Thermodynamics
Department of Mechanical Engineering
The City University, London

McGRAW-HILL Publishing Company Limited

LONDON · New York · Toronto · Sydney

Published by

McGRAW-HILL Publishing Company Limited
McGraw-Hill House · Maidenhead · Berkshire · England

07-094164-5

REPRINTED PHOTO LITHO BY JWA Ltd., BRISTOL

Preface

The aim of this book is to introduce the reader to the subject of heat transfer. It will take him sufficiently along the road to enable him to start reading profitably the many more extensive texts on the subject, and the latest research papers to be found in scientific periodicals. This book is therefore intended for students of engineering in universities and technical colleges, and it will also be of assistance to the practising engineer who needs a concise reference to the fundamental principles of the subject. The engineering student will find most, if not all, aspects of the subject taught in undergraduate courses and, thus equipped, he will be in a position to undertake further studies at postgraduate level.

SI units have been chosen as the primary system in this book. This choice was made because of the move to the metric system which is now in progress. Attention is also given to the British system, used in the majority of previous heat transfer literature, with conversion factors between the two sets of units. Both systems have been used for illustrative purposes in numerical examples in the text. An appendix of thermal property values in SI units is included.

Problems set at the end of each chapter are mostly from university examination papers. Since the subject matter in some of these problems covers more than one individual topic, the reader will find he is referred to a later chapter, as the need arises, for the necessary guidance to solve these problems.

It has been my aim throughout to introduce the principles of heat transfer in simple and logical steps. The need for an easily assimilated introduction to a subject becomes more urgent when the subject itself continues to grow at an ever increasing rate. I do not, of course, claim originality in the material presented; my purpose has been to select the topics necessary to give the beginner a view of the scope of the subject, and to present them as clearly as possible. I acknowledge my indebtedness to all those, past and present, who have contributed to the science of heat transfer with their original work, and as far as possible I have given detailed references at the end of

each chapter. I am also grateful to various persons and organiza-
tions for permission to use certain diagrams, tables, and photo-
graphs; credit for these is given at appropriate points throughout
the text.

The examination questions used were selected from papers of
Bristol, Cambridge, Glasgow, Leeds, London, Manchester, and
Oxford Universities. The source is stated at the end of each question.
The units used in some of the numerical problems have been con-
verted to the metric system, so that the reader may gain familiarity
with this system. I am indebted to the owners of the copyright of
these questions for permission to use them; permission was also
granted for the change of units to be made. It should be noted
that numerical answers quoted are my own responsibility, and the
universities concerned are in no way committed to approval of them.

The original manuscript was critically examined by Professor
G. D. S. MacLellan of the University of Leicester, and I am very
grateful to him for his constructive comments which have given the
text its final form. I must also acknowledge many fruitful discussions
with my colleagues at The City University which have helped in
numerous ways. Thanks are due particularly to Mr. B. M. Hayward
for his encouragement of the project.

Finally, I am deeply grateful to my indefatigable typist, my wife,
for all her careful work while coping with the younger generation.

John R. Simonson

Contents

Nomenclature

a	distance increment, area of cross-section
A	area
b, l, t	linear dimension
c	concentration
C	capacity ratio of heat exchanger
C, K	constants of integration
Cd	drag coefficient, or average friction factor
Cf	skin friction coefficient
c_p	specific heat at constant pressure
C_p	volumetric specific heat at constant pressure
d	diameter
D	diffusion coefficient
E	effectiveness of heat exchanger
f	friction factor
F	geometric configuration factor
$\mathscr{F}$	geometric emissivity factor
f_D	drag factor
g	gravitational acceleration
g	mass transfer per unit area and time
G	irradiation
h	convection coefficient
h_{fg}	latent enthalpy of evaporation
h_m	mass transfer coefficient
h_R	radiation coefficient
i	current density
I	current
I	intensity of radiation
J	radiosity
k	thermal conductivity
L, D, T, W	linear dimension
L_s	starting length
m	mass flow
n	coordinate direction
n	frequency of temperature variation
NTU	number of transfer units
$p, P, \Delta p$	pressure, difference of pressure
P	perimeter
q	heat transfer per unit area and time
q'	heat generation per unit volume and time

Q	heat transfer per unit time
r	radius, radial direction
r	residual value
R	resistance
R_m	universal gas constant
S_i	electrical shape factor
S_q	thermal shape factor
t	temperature
T	absolute temperature
$\mathbf{t}, \mathbf{\Delta t}$	time, time increment
U	overall heat transfer coefficient
U	velocity of temperature wave
v	velocity
v	specific volume
V	electrical potential
x, y, z	coordinate direction, linear dimension
X	length of temperature wave
α	thermal diffusivity
α	absorptivity
β	coefficient of cubical expansion
δ	boundary layer thickness
δ_b	thickness of laminar sub-boundary layer
δ_t	thermal boundary layer thickness
δ_t'	equivalent conducting film thickness
ε	emissivity
ε	eddy diffusivity
ε_q	eddy thermal diffusivity
ε_m	eddy mass diffusivity
η_f	fin effectiveness
η_{fe}	equivalent effectiveness of finned surface
θ	temperature difference
θ	angle in cylindrical coordinate system
λ	wave-length
μ	dynamic viscosity
v	kinematic viscosity
ρ	density
ρ	electrical resistivity
ρ	reflectivity
σ	Stefan–Boltzmann constant
τ	shear stress
τ	transmissivity
τ_t	turbulent shear stress

Dimensionless groups

Gr	Grashof number, $\beta g \theta \rho^2 l^3 / \mu^2$
J	Colburn J-factor, $St.\,Pr^{2/3}$
Le	Lewis number, D/α
Nu	Nusselt number, hl/k

Pr	Prandtl number, $c_p\mu/k$
Ra	Rayleigh number, $Gr.Pr$
Re	Reynolds number, $\rho vl/\mu$
Sc	Schmidt number, v/D
$(Sc)_\varepsilon$	turbulent Schmidt number, $\varepsilon/\varepsilon_m$
Sh	Sherwood number, $h_m l(p_j)_{lm}/DP$
St	Stanton number, $h/\rho vc_p$
$(St)_M$	mass transfer Stanton number, $Sh/(Re.Sc)$

Suffices

a	at axis of tube
a, w	air, water, (in hygrometry)
A	area
b	black body
b	limit of laminar sub-boundary layer
c	cold fluid
d	based on diameter
e	equivalent
f	fluid
h	hot fluid
i, j	components of mixture (in mass transfer)
i, o	inlet, outlet, (in heat exchangers)
L	length
m	mean value
n	direction of component
0	datum temperature
0	datum length
r	radial direction, or radial position
s	surroundings, of free stream
sat.	saturated temperature
t	temperature t
w	wall
x, y, z	direction of component
θ	angular component
λ	monochromatic

Superscript

—	average value

1

Introduction

One of the primary concerns of the engineer is the design and construction of machines many times more powerful than himself or any of his domestic animals. The development of this skill over the centuries has been fundamental to the growth of civilization. Man's early efforts to harness the power of wind and water owed very little to engineering science, and indeed the early steam engine was a practical reality *before* the science of thermodynamics was firmly established. In contrast, there is now a vast fund of engineering knowledge behind the present day prime movers.

Much engineering activity is directed to the controlled release of power from fossil and nuclear fuels, and with making that power available where it is needed. The laws of heat transfer are of the utmost importance in these activities. The generation of power from the energy changes of chemical and nuclear reactions involves vast quantities of thermal energy needing direction. Further, chemical processes of combustion yield temperatures at which most constructional materials would melt; adequate protection by heat transfer processes is therefore vital. The distribution of energy as electricity is accompanied, at all stages, by certain wastages manifested as rising temperature of the equipment. Heat transfer considerations enable these temperatures to be controlled within safe limits.

The laws of heat transfer find application in many other fields of engineering. Chemical and process engineering, and manufacturing and metallurgical industries are examples. In addition, the civil and constructional engineer and environment control engineer need considerable knowledge of the subject. Large city buildings must be economically heated and insulated, and air conditioning is increasingly necessary.

To the mechanical engineer heat transfer is a subject closely allied to applied thermodynamics. The first and second laws of

1

thermodynamics state the relations between the physical entities of heat and work, and the limit to the amount of work that may be obtained from any source of heat. Even this limit cannot be reached in practical engineering processes because of their inherent irreversibility. These irreversibilities may be accounted for in calculations but, even so, thermodynamics alone leaves a lot of questions unanswered. There is no time scale and, consequently, thermodynamics will not permit the calculation of physical sizes necessary to achieve a given objective. In a steam power plant it is necessary to transfer the thermal energy of the hot combustion gases of the burnt fuel to the water in the boiler tubes. The actual rate of transfer to produce a required flow rate of steam may be known, but without the laws of heat transfer and knowledge of the properties of the engineering materials to be used, it is not possible to calculate the size and surface area of the tubes required. From an economic point of view, the boiler must be made as small as possible, hence the heat transfer rate must be as high as possible. Elsewhere in the plant, heat transfer considerations are necessary in insulating the steam delivery lines and in condensing the low pressure turbine exhaust.

Heat transfer processes, then, are described by equations which relate the energy to be transferred in unit time to the physical area involved. Other factors entering the equations are the temperatures, or the temperature gradient, and some coefficient which depends on various physical properties of the system and on the particular mechanism of heat transfer involved. Three basic mechanisms of heat transfer are recognized. They may occur separately, or simultaneously. Separate equations may be written to describe each mechanism, and when two or more mechanisms occur simultaneously it is sometimes possible to add the separate effects; but sometimes it is necessary to consider the equations of the participating mechanisms together. The subject matter thus conveniently sub-divides itself into the separate basic mechanisms of heat transfer, and the combinations of them.

Heat is transferred by conduction, convection, and radiation. Before describing these processes, it is desirable to clarify what is meant by 'heat'. In the study of thermodynamics, heat is recognized as an interaction between communicating systems, arising solely from a temperature difference. Thus a heat transfer is strictly a phenomenon occurring only at *boundaries* of systems, and a heat transfer elsewhere in a system is more correctly a redistribution of internal energy within the system. As it is convenient to keep to the conventional language of heat transfer, this should be kept in mind, and the word heat will not in most cases be in accord with the thermodynamic usage.

Conduction is the mode of heat transfer in a solid material and occurs by virtue of a temperature difference between different parts of the material. Conduction also occurs in liquids and gases but is generally associated also with convection, and possibly with radiation as well in the case of gases. Conduction within a solid is a transfer of internal energy; this energy is, in fact, energy of motion of the constituent molecules, atoms, and particles of which the material consists. The kinetic energy of the motion is proportional to the absolute temperature; molecular collisions lead to energy transfer to regions of lower kinetic energy. Under steady conditions a molecule will pass on the same amount of energy that it receives. Under non-steady conditions the flow of energy is governed by the changing energy levels.

The theory of conduction heat transfer was established by Joseph Fourier whose work was published in Paris in 1822,[1] but pioneer work was done by Biot in 1804[2] and 1816.[3] Conduction is described by an equation known as the Fourier rate equation

$$Q_x = -kA\frac{dt}{dx} \qquad (1.1)$$

The rate of heat flow (in only the x-direction, see Fig. 1.1) is proportional to the product of the area of flow and the temperature gradient, the constant of proportionality being the thermal conductivity k which is a property of the material. The negative sign results from the convention of defining a positive heat flow in the direction of a negative temperature gradient.

The units involved depend on the system chosen. (See the Appendix for a discussion of units.) In the SI metric system, units of heat transfer are joules/second, J/s, with the area in m^2 and the temperature gradient in deg C/m. Thus, the units of k are J/m s deg C. In the British system of units, used in the majority of existing heat transfer literature in the English speaking world, the units of heat transfer are Btu/h, with the area in ft^2 and the temperature gradient in deg F/ft. Hence k has units of Btu/ft h deg F.

Conduction in fluids generally forms a very small part of the total heat transfer, convection being the predominating mechanism.

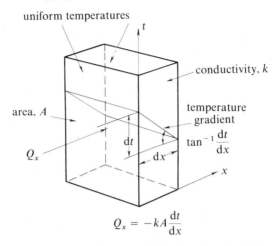

Fig. 1.1. *Fourier's law applied to one-dimensional conduction in a plane slab of material.*

Convection is the name given to the gross motion of the fluid itself, so that fresh fluid is continually available for heating or cooling. Apart from the bulk movement of the fluid, there is generally a smaller motion of eddies which further assists in distributing heat energy. Convection heat transfer is sub-divided into two different kinds, natural and forced. Heat transfer by *natural convection* occurs between a solid and a fluid undisturbed by other effects when there is a temperature difference between the two, as in a kettle of water. It is not often that a fluid can be regarded as entirely at rest, so frequently there is a small amount of forced convection as well. But true *forced convection* requires a major applied motion of the fluid in relation to the source or sink of heat, so that natural convection effects are negligible. An important aspect of natural convection is that the fluid motion which does occur is due entirely to natural buoyancy forces arising from a changing density of the fluid in the vicinity of the surface. Within the realms of both natural and forced convection there are two sub-divisions of laminar and turbulent flow convection. In forced convection there are also special cases where the flow may be separated from the solid surface, as in flow across the outside of a pipe, and also convection with a phase change occurring in the fluid. This is, of course, encountered in steam raising and condensing plant.

It is thus evident that many factors enter into heat convection, including the shape and magnitude of the solid–fluid boundary, characteristics of the fluid flow, such as the magnitude of turbulent eddies, and the conductivity of the fluid itself.

Because of these complexities many convection problems are not amenable to mathematical solution, and recourse is made to techniques of dimensional analysis and experiment. Thus many empirical dimensionless relationships are now available in the literature to enable the engineer to design his heat transfer apparatus, whether it be an industrial heat exchanger or domestic convector.

Newton (1701)[4] proposed a general equation to describe convection heat transfer,

$$Q = hA(t_1 - t_2) \qquad (1.2)$$

Figure 1.2 indicates that heat transfer is occurring from a surface of area A at temperature t_1 to a fluid at a lower temperature t_2.

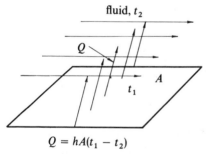

$$Q = hA(t_1 - t_2)$$

Fig. 1.2. Diagrammatic representation of convection from a flat plate, illustrating the use of Newton's equation.

h is the convection coefficient and has the units J/m^2 s deg C in the SI metric system, or Btu/ft^2 h deg F in the British system. It takes care of the many factors entering a particular example of convection, and the value of h will vary for differing flow regimes, fluid properties, and temperature differences. The main problem in the analysis of convection is to predict values of h for design purposes. The value of h in different regimes and for different fluids is generally within the ranges indicated in Table 1.1.

The third mode of heat transfer known as radiation is rather different in nature to the first two. Conduction and convection

Table 1.1

Convection system	Range of h,* J/m^2 s deg C
Natural convection	3·5–50
Forced convection (air)	10–550
Forced convection (liquids)	100–5500
Boiling heat transfer (water)	1000–110,000
Condensation (steam, filmwise)	550–25,000
Forced convection (liquid metals)	3000–110,000

* For numerical conversion factors, see the Appendix

occur within solid or fluid material and often are present simultaneously. In contrast, radiation is an energy transfer between bodies and occurs most freely through a vacuum between those bodies. All bodies at temperatures above absolute zero emit electromagnetic waves of various wave-lengths. Visible light together with infra-red and ultra-violet radiation forms but a small part of the total electromagnetic spectrum. The mechanism by which radiation is propagated is not of any direct concern to the mechanical engineer, who is mostly interested in overall effects rather than in molecular detail. It is sufficient to say that radiation is energy emitted by vibrating electrons in the molecules of material at the surface of a body, and the amount emitted depends on the absolute temperature of the body.

The third equation to be introduced at this stage dates from 1884 when the work of Boltzmann[5] consolidated the earlier work of Stefan (1879).[6] Known as the Stefan–Boltzmann equation, it is

$$Q = \sigma A T^4 \qquad (1.3)$$

where T is the absolute temperature, A is the surface area of a perfectly radiating body and σ is the Stefan–Boltzmann constant and has the value of $5·663 \times 10^{-8}$ J/m^2 s (deg K)^4, or $0·171 \times 10^{-8}$ Btu/ft^2 h (deg R)^4. Stefan established this relationship experimentally, while Boltzmann proved it theoretically. A perfectly radiating or black body emits at any given temperature the maximum possible energy at all wave-lengths. The energy emitted will be less for real materials. The equation is different from the first two in that it does not define a heat exchange. Such an equation could be written in analogous form to (1.2). The emitting and absorbing characteristics of surfaces, and the 'view' that surfaces have of each other, are factors which enter the consideration of radiation exchanges.

REFERENCES

1. Fourier, J. B. *Théorie analytique de la chaleur*, Paris, 1822. Translated by A. Freeman, Dover Publications, New York, 1955.
2. Biot, J. B. *Bibliothèque Britannique*, Vol. 27, 310 (1804).
3. Biot, J. B. *Traité de physique*, Vol. 4, 669 (1816).
4. Newton, I. *Phil. Trans., Roy. Soc.*, London, Vol. 22, 824 (1701).
5. Boltzmann, L. *Wiedemanns Annalen*, Vol. 22, 291 (1884).
6. Stefan, J. *Sitzungsber. Akad. Wiss. Wien. Math.-naturw. Kl.*, Vol. 79, 391 (1879).

Section 1
Heat Transfer by Conduction

2

The equations of heat conduction

Before considering the equations by which heat conduction is described, it is necessary first to stress further aspects of the nature of the conduction process.

2.1. The Nature of Heat Conduction

The Fourier equation of heat conduction (1.1) has already been introduced. This equation is for one-dimensional heat flow, and may be written in a more general form:

$$Q_n = -kA \frac{\partial t}{\partial n} \qquad (2.1)$$

where Q_n is the rate of heat conduction in the n-direction, and $\partial t/\partial n$ is the temperature gradient in that direction. The partial derivative is used since there may exist temperature gradients in other directions. One-dimensional conduction does not often occur in practice since a body would have to be either perfectly insulated at its edges or so large that conduction would be one-dimensional at the centre.

Equation (2.1) is for steady state heat transfer, i.e., the rate of heat flow does not vary with time. It may be re-written

$$q_n = \frac{Q_n}{A} = -k \frac{\partial t}{\partial n} \qquad (2.2)$$

where q_n is the heat flux in heat units per unit time and per unit area in the n-direction. This is a vector quantity since it has magnitude and direction. The greatest heat flux between two isothermal surfaces will always occur along the normal to those surfaces.

Heat conduction within a solid may be visualized as a heat flux which varies in direction and position throughout the material. This follows from the fact that temperature within the solid is a

11

function of position coordinates of the system (e.g., x, y, z). In addition, temperature may be a function of time, (**t**), so in general $t = f(x, y, z, \mathbf{t})$.

The problem of determining the magnitude of heat conduction resolves itself to finding first the isotherms within the system and the way in which their positions vary with time. In steady state conduction the isotherms remain stationary with time, and one may visualize a large number of isothermal surfaces throughout the system, each an increment in temperature apart. The heat flux normal to any one surface will vary with position depending on the distance between surfaces. It is then necessary to sum the heat flow through one isothermal surface only since, in steady state, the total heat flow through any two isothermal surfaces must be the same. In unsteady conduction the problem is complicated by the fact that isothermal surfaces are no longer fixed, and the rate at which heat is being stored must be taken into account.

Before taking the first step, which is to develop the equation for temperature as a function of position and time, it is opportune to introduce some facts about different conducting materials.

Solid materials may be divided into two groups, metallic and non-metallic, for which there is a marked contrast in the values of conductivity. The Appendix lists properties for some of the more useful materials. The high values of conductivity of metals are attributable to the well ordered crystalline structure of the material. The close arrangement of molecules permits a rapid transfer of energy and, in addition, free electrons play a considerable part. Metals such as copper and silver which conduct electricity also conduct heat well. There is, in fact, a marked similarity between conduction heat transfer and the flow of electricity, and the electrical analogy is often used in the solution of conduction problems.

In contrast, non-metals do not have a well ordered crystalline structure and, in addition, are often porous in nature. Thus energy transfer between molecules is seriously impeded, and the values of conductivity are much lower. The small pores within the material, being full of air, further restrict the flow of heat since gases are poor conductors. This is because molecules of a gas are relatively widely spaced and the transfer of energy depends on collisions between these molecules.

The thermal conductivities of most substances vary with temperature, and for accuracy such variation should be allowed for in conduction problems. However, this is a complication which may be ignored in an introductory study of the subject because the variation with temperature is not great. Over a reasonable temperature range the relationship between conductivity k_t and temperature t may be assumed linear:

$$k_t = k_0(1 \pm \alpha t) \qquad (2.3)$$

where k_0 is the conductivity at temperature t_0, and α is a constant. In most practical applications it is sufficient to assume a mean constant value for conductivity.

A complication more serious than temperature variation of conductivity occurs in certain engineering materials, viz., that conductivity may vary with the direction of heat flow. This arises commonly in laminated materials used in electrical engineering. Thus the conductivity parallel to the laminates is different to the value perpendicular to the laminates. Most types of wood also exhibit this property, the conductivity parallel to the grain being different to that across the grain. Conducting materials are classified according to whether or not they have this property, and are known as anisotropic and isotropic materials respectively. For anisotropic materials the analysis of conduction is more difficult and is not included in this introductory text. The basic ideas are given by Eckert and Drake,[1] and the general treatment may be found in the work of Carslaw and Jaeger.[2]

Differential equations of the temperature field will now be developed in two coordinate systems, rectangular and cylindrical.

2.2. The Differential Equation of Conduction in a Rectangular Coordinate System

The material of the system is assumed to be isotropic and the conductivity is assumed invariable with temperature. Consider the infinitesimal element of the material represented by the volume $dx\,dy\,dz$ in Fig. 2.1. The heat flowing into and out of the element is resolved in the x-, y- and z-directions. Thus from the Fourier equation the rate of heat flowing into the element in the x-direction is

$$dQ_x = -k\,dy\,dz\,\frac{\partial t}{\partial x}$$

since the area of flow normal to the x-direction is $dy\,dz$ and the

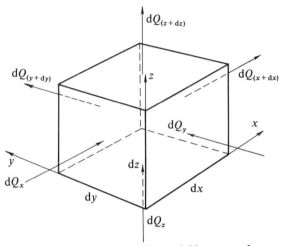

Fig. 2.1.   Conduction in an element of material in rectangular coordinates.

temperature gradient is $\partial t/\partial x$. The rate of heat flowing out of the element in the x-direction is

$$dQ_{(x+dx)} = -k\,dy\,dz\,\frac{\partial}{\partial x}\left(t + \frac{\partial t}{\partial x}dx\right)$$

$$= -k\,dy\,dz\,\frac{\partial t}{\partial x} - k\,dx\,dy\,dz\,\frac{\partial^2 t}{\partial x^2}$$

Therefore the net rate of heat flow into the element in the x-direction is

$$dQ_x - dQ_{(x+dx)} = k\,dx\,dy\,dz\,\frac{\partial^2 t}{\partial x^2} \qquad (2.4)$$

In a similar manner, the net rates of heat flow into the element in the y- and z-directions are given by

$$dQ_y - dQ_{(y+dy)} = k\,dx\,dy\,dz\,\frac{\partial^2 t}{\partial y^2} \qquad (2.5)$$

$$dQ_z - dQ_{(z+dz)} = k\,dx\,dy\,dz\,\frac{\partial^2 t}{\partial z^2} \qquad (2.6)$$

The total rate of heat flow into the element is the sum of the right-hand sides of equations (2.4), (2.5), and (2.6), which is

$$k\,dx\,dy\,dz\left(\frac{\partial^2 t}{\partial x^2} + \frac{\partial^2 t}{\partial y^2} + \frac{\partial^2 t}{\partial z^2}\right)$$

In addition to heat flowing into and out of the element, the possibilities of heat being generated within the element, (e.g., due to the flow of electricity) and of heat being stored within the element (as in the case of unsteady conduction), have to be considered.

If q' is the rate at which heat is generated per unit volume, the rate of heat generation within the element is

$$q' \, dx \, dy \, dz$$

The rate at which heat is being stored within the element is governed by the rate of temperature change $\partial t / \partial t$. If ρ is the density of the material and c_p the specific heat at constant pressure, the rate of heat storage will be

$$dx \, dy \, dz \, \rho c_p \frac{\partial t}{\partial t}$$

This assumes the element may expand or contract freely at constant pressure. The rate at which heat is being stored within the element is equal to the sum of the net rate of heat flow into the element and the rate of heat generation within it, hence:

$$\rho c_p \frac{\partial t}{\partial t} = k \left(\frac{\partial^2 t}{\partial x^2} + \frac{\partial^2 t}{\partial y^2} + \frac{\partial^2 t}{\partial z^2} \right) + q'$$

$$\therefore \quad \frac{\partial t}{\partial t} = \alpha \left(\frac{\partial^2 t}{\partial x^2} + \frac{\partial^2 t}{\partial y^2} + \frac{\partial^2 t}{\partial z^2} \right) + \frac{q'}{\rho c_p} \qquad (2.7)$$

where $\alpha = k / \rho c_p$ and is known as the thermal diffusivity of the material. It is a ratio of the heat conduction to heat storage qualities of the material.

Equation (2.7) is the general differential equation of conduction in a rectangular coordinate system and may be simplified to suit any particular application. Thus the equation for unsteady conduction in one dimension without heat generation is

$$\frac{\partial t}{\partial t} = \alpha \left(\frac{\partial^2 t}{\partial x^2} \right) \qquad (2.8)$$

since q', $\partial^2 t / \partial y^2$ and $\partial^2 t / \partial z^2$ are equal to 0.

For any problem of steady conduction, $\partial t / \partial t = 0$, since there is then no variation of temperature with time. The equations for

two- and one-dimensional steady conduction with heat generation
are

$$0 = \alpha\left(\frac{\partial^2 t}{\partial x^2} + \frac{\partial^2 t}{\partial y^2}\right) + \frac{q'}{\rho c_p} \tag{2.9}$$

and

$$0 = \alpha\left(\frac{d^2 t}{dx^2}\right) + \frac{q'}{\rho c_p} \tag{2.10}$$

it being permissible to use the total derivative in the one-dimensional
case. In the absence of heat generation the equations reduce to

$$0 = \alpha\left(\frac{\partial^2 t}{\partial x^2} + \frac{\partial^2 t}{\partial y^2}\right) \quad \text{and} \quad 0 = \alpha\left(\frac{d^2 t}{dx^2}\right)$$

and, consequently,

$$\frac{\partial^2 t}{\partial x^2} + \frac{\partial^2 t}{\partial y^2} = 0 \tag{2.11}$$

and

$$\frac{d^2 t}{dx^2} = 0 \tag{2.12}$$

Problems involving equations (2.8) to (2.12) will be considered in
later chapters.

2.3. The Differential Equation of Conduction in a Cylindrical Coordinate System

Often, conduction problems involve heat flow in solid or hollow
round bars and, consequently, the cylindrical coordinate system,
Fig. 2.2, is used. The general approach is exactly the same as before
except that heat flows in radial, circumferential, and axial directions
have now to be considered. The element to be considered is $r d\theta\, dr\, dz$.
Heat flowing into the element in the radial direction is

$$dQ_r = -k\, dz\, rd\theta\, \frac{\partial t}{\partial r}$$

and out of the element in the radial direction,

$$dQ_{(r+dr)} = -k\, dz(r + dr)\, d\theta\, \frac{\partial}{\partial r}\left(t + \frac{\partial t}{\partial r}\, dr\right)$$

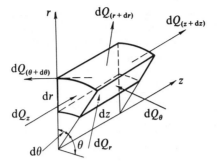

Fig. 2.2. *Conduction in an element of material in cylindrical coordinates.*

Hence

$$dQ_r - dQ_{(r+dr)} = k\, dz\, dr\, d\theta \frac{\partial t}{\partial r} + k\, dz\, rd\theta \frac{\partial^2 t}{\partial r^2}\, dr \qquad (2.13)$$

neglecting a term of higher order.

In a similar manner, the net heat flowing into the element in the circumferential direction is found to be

$$dQ_\theta - dQ_{(\theta+d\theta)} = k\, dr\, dz\, \frac{\partial^2 t}{r^2 \partial \theta^2}\, rd\theta \qquad (2.14)$$

and, in the axial direction,

$$dQ_z - dQ_{(z+dz)} = k\, dr\, rd\theta \frac{\partial^2 t}{\partial z^2}\, dz \qquad (2.15)$$

The rate of heat generation within the element is

$$q'\, rd\theta\, dr\, dz$$

and the rate at which heat is being stored within the element is

$$rd\theta\, dr\, dz\, \rho c_p \frac{\partial t}{\partial t}$$

Then an energy balance for the element leads to the general differential equation for heat flow in three dimensions in a cylindrical coordinate system, i.e.,

$$\frac{\partial t}{\partial t} = \alpha \left(\frac{\partial^2 t}{\partial r^2} + \frac{1}{r} \frac{\partial t}{\partial r} + \frac{1}{r^2} \frac{\partial^2 t}{\partial \theta^2} + \frac{\partial^2 t}{\partial z^2} \right) + \frac{q'}{\rho c_p} \qquad (2.16)$$

This equation may similarly be simplified to suit any particular problem. Steady one-dimensional heat flow in the radial direction only will be considered in later chapters. With heat generation within the material the equation is

$$\alpha\left(\frac{d^2 t}{dr^2} + \frac{1}{r}\frac{dt}{dr}\right) + \frac{q'}{\rho c_p} = 0 \tag{2.17}$$

and without heat generation,

$$\frac{d^2 t}{dr^2} + \frac{1}{r}\frac{dt}{dr} = 0 \tag{2.18}$$

PROBLEM

Show that the general equation of heat conduction in spherical coordinates is given by

$$\frac{\partial t}{\partial t} = \alpha\left[\frac{\partial^2 t}{\partial r^2} + \frac{2}{r}\frac{\partial t}{\partial r} + \frac{1}{r^2 \sin\phi}\frac{\partial}{\partial\phi}\left(\sin\phi\frac{\partial t}{\partial\phi}\right) + \frac{1}{r^2 \sin^2\phi}\frac{\partial^2 t}{\partial\theta^2}\right] + \frac{q'}{\rho c_p}$$

and transform the equation in rectangular coordinates (2.7) into spherical coordinates by making the substitutions

$$x = r \sin\phi\cos\theta$$

$$y = r \sin\phi\sin\theta$$

$$z = r \cos\phi$$

REFERENCES

1. Eckert, E. R. G., and Drake, R. M. *Introduction to the Transfer of Heat and Mass*, 2nd ed., McGraw-Hill, New York (1959).
2. Carslaw, H. S., and Jaeger, J.C. *Conduction of Heat in Solids*, Oxford University Press (1947).

3

One-dimensional steady state conduction

The simplest example of steady state conduction in one dimension is the transfer of heat through a single plane slab. Many simple problems, such as conduction through the wall of a building, approximate to this.

3.1. Conduction in Plane Slabs

To calculate the heat transfer in a single slab, Fourier's law applied to an infinitesimal layer within the slab, Fig. 3.1, may be integrated directly. Thus

$$Q_x = - kA \frac{dt}{dx}$$

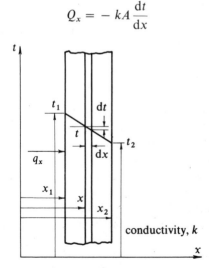

Fig. 3.1. One-dimensional steady state conduction in a plane slab.

19

and hence

$$Q_x = \frac{-kA(t_2 - t_1)}{(x_2 - x_1)} \tag{3.1}$$

where $(x_2 - x_1)$ is the thickness of the slab and A is the area of the slab. Using consistent units, the heat transfer calculated will be in heat units per unit time.

The same result will be obtained if the appropriate differential equation is integrated. Integration twice of equation (2.12),

$$\frac{d^2t}{dx^2} = 0$$

gives

$$t = C_1x + C_2 \tag{3.2}$$

where C_1 and C_2 are constants of integration to be determined from the boundary conditions, i.e., the temperatures at x_1 and x_2. Equation (3.2) indicates that the temperature variation through the slab is linear. The temperature gradient from equation (3.2) used in Fourier's law gives equation (3.1). Equation (3.1) may be re-written as

$$\frac{Q_x}{A} = q_x = \frac{-k(t_2 - t_1)}{x_2 - x_1}, \tag{3.3}$$

in which form it may be compared with Ohm's law describing the flow of electricity, i.e.,

$$\text{Current density } (i) = \frac{(V_1 - V_2)}{\rho(x_2 - x_1)}, \qquad \frac{\text{Potential difference}}{\text{Resistance of unit area}}$$

where ρ is the resistivity of the material, in units of ohms × length. The heat flux q_x is analogous to current density i; the temperature drop $-(t_2 - t_1)$ is analogous to potential difference $(V_1 - V_2)$; and the resistance per unit area to heat transfer, $(x_2 - x_1)/k$, is analogous to electrical resistance per unit area, $\rho(x_2 - x_1)$. The usefulness of this similarity will be made more apparent later.

Conduction through a system of plane slabs of different material has often to be considered. A partition wall comprising two layers of plaster board separated by a thickness of glass-fibre insulation, or a furnace wall consisting of a layer of fire brick and a layer of insulating brick, are typical examples. Further, such a system may separate two fluids of different temperatures, when the actual wall temperatures are not known. The processes of heat transfer between the wall surfaces and the adjacent fluid are by convection and radiation. Figure 3.2 shows such a system. The Newton equation for convection may be written as

$$q_c = - h_c(t_f - t_w) \tag{3.4}$$

In this equation, q_c is the heat flux due to convection at the solid/fluid interface, and t_w is the wall temperature and t_f the fluid temperature. The region in the fluid where the temperature changes from t_f to t_w is known as the boundary layer. h_c is the convection coefficient and is assumed known. Its determination forms the subject matter of Section 2, where the suffix c is dropped.

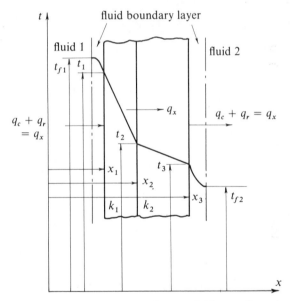

Fig. 3.2. *A multiple plane slab separating two fluids, one-dimensional steady state conduction.*

A similar equation may be written to express the radiation exchange between the wall and the fluid or some surface beyond the fluid, such as another wall.

$$q_r = - h_R(t_s - t_w) \tag{3.5}$$

t_s is the temperature of the surface receiving a net radiation exchange and for simplicity is assumed to be the same as the fluid temperature. h_R is the radiation coefficient and is assumed known. Further reference to radiation coefficients is made in Section 4.

The total heat flow or conduction flux q_x from the wall by convection and radiation is found by adding (3.4) and (3.5):

$$q_x = q_c + q_r = - h_c(t_f - t_w) - h_R(t_s - t_w)$$

$$= - (h_c + h_R)(t_f - t_w) \qquad (3.6)$$

A multiple slab of two layers of conductivities k_1 and k_2 which separates two fluids f_1 and f_2 at temperatures t_{f1} and t_{f2} is now considered. For exchange between fluid f_1 and wall surface at t_1:

$$q_x = - (h_c + h_R)_{f1}(t_1 - t_{f1}) \qquad (3.7)$$

For conduction through the two layers of material:

$$q_x = \frac{- k_1(t_2 - t_1)}{x_2 - x_1} = \frac{- k_2(t_3 - t_2)}{x_3 - x_2} \qquad (3.8)$$

For exchange between the wall surface at t_3 and the fluid f_2:

$$q_x = - (h_c + h_R)_{f2}(t_{f2} - t_3) \qquad (3.9)$$

Re-arranging and adding:

$$q_x \left[\frac{1}{(h_c + h_R)_{f1}} + \frac{x_2 - x_1}{k_1} + \frac{x_3 - x_2}{k_2} + \frac{1}{(h_c + h_R)_{f2}} \right]$$

$$= - (t_{f2} - t_{f1})$$

and hence

$$q_x = - U(t_{f2} - t_{f1}) \qquad (3.10)$$

where

$$\frac{1}{U} = \frac{1}{(h_c + h_R)_{f1}} + \frac{x_2 - x_1}{k_1} + \frac{x_3 - x_2}{k_2} + \frac{1}{(h_c + h_R)_{f2}} \qquad (3.11)$$

$1/U$ is the overall thermal resistance per unit area between fluids and U is the overall heat transfer coefficient. The resistances to heat flow due to convection and radiation act in parallel and the resistances due to the conducting layers act in series. The heat flow may be calculated from (3.10) and (3.11), and interface temperatures from (3.7), (3.8), and (3.9).

EXAMPLE 3.1

A cold storage room has walls constructed of 0·23 m brick on the outside, 0·08 m of plastic foam and finally 1·5 cm of wood on the inside. The air temperature outside is constant at 22°C and the air temperature inside is constant at −2°C. If the convection coefficient, wood to air, is 29 J/m² s deg C, and the convection coefficient, air to brick is 12 J/m² s deg C, and thermal conductivities of wood, foam, and brick are 0·17, 0·024, 0·98 J/m s deg C respectively, determine the overall heat transfer coefficient air to air, the energy to be removed by refrigeration in 24 hours if the total wall area is 90 m², and the temperature of the inside surface of the brick.

Solution

$$\frac{1}{U} = \frac{1}{12} + \frac{0·23}{0·98} + \frac{0·08}{0·024} + \frac{1·5}{100 \times 0·17} + \frac{1}{29}$$

$$= 0·0834 + 0·235 + 3·34 + 0·0883 + 0·0345$$

$$= 3·78$$

$$U = 0·265 \text{ J/m}^2 \text{ s deg C}$$

The energy transfer in 24 hours is

$$0·265(22 + 2) \times 90 \times 3600 \times 24 = 4·95 \times 10^7 \text{ Joules.}$$

The heat flux is $0·265 \times (22 + 2) = 6·36 \text{ J/m}^2 \text{ s.}$
A coefficient between the external air and the inside surface of the brick is given by

$$\frac{1}{U} = \frac{1}{12} + \frac{0·23}{0·98} = 0·3184$$

$$U = 3·14$$

The temperature of the inside surface of the brick, t, is given by

$$6·36 = 3·14(22 - t)$$

hence

$$t = 20·0°C$$

3.2. Effect of a Variable Conductivity in a Plane Slab

In considering the variation of k with temperature in the case of one-dimensional flow in a plane slab, equation (2.3) for the relationship between k and temperature will be used.

For conduction in a single plane slab,

$$q_x = -k_0(1 \pm \alpha t)\frac{dt}{dx}$$

$$\therefore \quad q_x(x_2 - x_1) = -k_0\left[(t_2 - t_1) \mp \frac{\alpha}{2}(t_2^2 - t_1^2)\right]$$

$$= \frac{-2k_0[2(t_2 - t_1) \pm \alpha(t_2 - t_1)(t_2 + t_1)]}{2}$$

and

$$q_x = -k_0\frac{[2 \pm \alpha(t_2 + t_1)](t_2 - t_1)}{2(x_2 - x_1)} \qquad (3.12)$$

It will be found that equation (3.12) can also be obtained by taking an average of the conductivities at temperatures t_2 and t_1 and substituting into equation (3.3). Equation (3.12) may be used to find the interface temperature between two plane slabs, e.g., for two materials where $k_{1t} = k_{10}(1 + \alpha t)$ and $k_{2t} = k_{20}(1 + \beta t)$. The heat flux through both slabs is the same, hence

$$-k_{10}\frac{[2 + \alpha(t_2 + t_1)](t_2 - t_1)}{2(x_2 - x_1)} = -k_{20}\frac{[2 + \beta(t_3 + t_2)](t_3 - t_2)}{2(x_3 - x_2)}$$

This equation may be solved to find t_2, and then q_x may be calculated.

3.3. Radial Conduction in Cylindrical Layers

Conduction through thick walled pipes is a common heat transfer problem, and may be treated one-dimensionally if surface temperatures are uniform. The heat flow is then in the radial direction only. Figure 3.3 illustrates the situation for a single layer. Fourier's law may be applied to a cylindrical layer at radius r:

$$Q_r = -kA\frac{dt}{dr}$$

Here A is the surface area at the radius r, and obviously A will vary between the inner and outer radii. It is therefore convenient to consider a unit length of cylinder, when the radial heat transfer is

$$Q_r = -k(2\pi r)\frac{dt}{dr} \qquad (3.13)$$

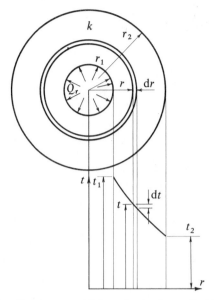

Fig. 3.3.   Steady state radial conduction in a cylindrical layer.

$2\pi r$ is the area per unit length. Since the same quantity Q_r is flowing through a steadily increasing cylindrical area, the temperature gradient must decrease with increasing radius. Integrating:

$$Q_r \ln \frac{r_2}{r_1} = -2\pi k(t_2 - t_1)$$

$$\therefore \quad Q_r = -2\pi k \frac{(t_2 - t_1)}{\ln r_2/r_1} \tag{3.14}$$

By analogy with Ohm's law, the thermal resistance per unit length of cylinder in this case is $(1/2\pi k)\ln(r_2/r_1)$.

Equation (3.14) may also be derived from the general equation for the cylindrical coordinate system (2.16) which simplifies to

$$\frac{d^2 t}{dr^2} + \frac{1}{r}\frac{dt}{dr} = 0 \tag{(2.18)}$$

for the case of steady radial conduction in the absence of internal heat generation. This equation may be integrated to give

$$t = C_3 \ln r + C_4 \tag{3.15}$$

where C_3 and C_4 are constants of integration to be found from boundary conditions. Thus, if $t = t_1$ at $r = r_1$ and $t = t_2$ at $r = r_2$, it is found that

$$t = \frac{(t_2 - t_1)}{\ln r_2/r_1} \ln \frac{r}{r_1} + t_1 \tag{3.16}$$

To obtain equation (3.14), the temperature gradient is found by differentiating (3.16) and substituting back in (3.13).

A thick walled steam pipe with lagging is a familiar example of multiple cylindrical layers, and the treatment is similar to the multiple plane layer. Figure 3.4 shows two cylindrical layers separating two fluids f_1 and f_2. It is assumed that heat transfer at the surfaces is in each case predominantly by convection. Considering unit length, at the inside surface:

$$Q_r = -2\pi r_1 h_{c1}(t_1 - t_{f1})$$

The same quantity is conducted through the two layers, hence

$$Q_r = -2\pi k_1 \frac{(t_2 - t_1)}{\ln r_2/r_1} = -2\pi k_2 \frac{(t_3 - t_2)}{\ln r_3/r_2}$$

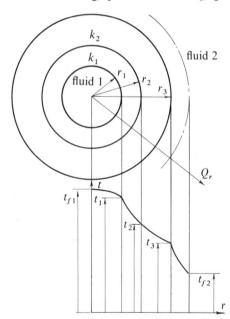

Fig. 3.4. *Steady state radial conduction in concentric cylinders separating two fluids.*

It is also convected from the outside surface, so

$$Q_r = -2\pi r_3 h_{c2}(t_{f2} - t_3)$$

Re-arranging and adding these equations gives:

$$Q_r\left(\frac{1}{2\pi r_1 h_{c1}} + \frac{\ln r_2/r_1}{2\pi k_1} + \frac{\ln r_3/r_2}{2\pi k_2} + \frac{1}{2\pi r_3 h_{c2}}\right) = -(t_{f2} - t_{f1})$$

or

$$Q_r = -U(t_{f2} - t_{f1}) \tag{3.17}$$

where

$$\frac{1}{U} = \frac{1}{2\pi r_1 h_{c1}} + \frac{\ln r_2/r_1}{2\pi k_1} + \frac{\ln r_3/r_2}{2\pi k_2} + \frac{1}{2\pi r_3 h_{c2}}$$

As before, U is the overall heat transfer coefficient between the two fluids and $1/U$ represents the thermal resistance per unit length and consists of the sum of individual thermal resistances to conducted and convected heat flow.

3.4. Critical Thickness of Insulation

As already mentioned, an important application of the multiple cylindrical layer system is the insulated pipe, where the outer conducting layer is the insulation, made of a material of low conductivity. One might expect that increasing the thickness of insulation would invariably reduce the heat loss from the pipe. However, this is not so, and it is possible under certain conditions actually to increase it.

Adapting equation (3.17) to the nomenclature of Fig. 3.5:

$$Q_r = \frac{-(t_0 - t_i)}{\dfrac{1}{2\pi r_0 h} + \dfrac{\ln r_0/r_i}{2\pi k}} \tag{3.18}$$

is obtained. This considers the temperature difference $(t_i - t_0)$, and assumes t_i is constant, and h is constant with radius and temperature of the outer surface. The heat flow per unit length, Q_r, will be a maximum when the denominator is a minimum. The denominator will have a minimum value at a certain critical radius $r_{0,\,crit.}$, r_i

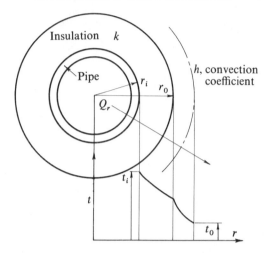

Fig. 3.5.   The insulated pipe problem.

being constant. This minimum value can be found by putting

$$\frac{d}{dr_0}\left(\frac{1}{2\pi r_0 h} + \frac{\ln r_0/r_i}{2\pi k}\right) = 0$$

$$\therefore \qquad -\frac{1}{r_0^2 h} + \frac{1}{k r_0} = 0$$

The corresponding value of r_0 is $r_{0,\,crit.}$, hence

$$r_0 = \frac{k}{h} = r_{0,\,crit.} \tag{3.19}$$

It can be proved that the denominator has a minimum, and not maximum, value by taking the second derivative with respect to r_0, which will be found to be positive. Inspection of (3.18) shows that $1/2\pi r_0 h$ is the thermal resistance per unit length due to convection and that this decreases with increasing r_0, and $\dfrac{\ln r_0/r_i}{2\pi k}$ is the thermal resistance per unit length of the insulating material which increases with r_0. At $r_{0,\,crit.}$ the rate of increase of insulation resistance is equal to the rate of decrease of convection resistance, thus giving the minimum overall thermal resistance. The variation of heat flow, Q_r, with r_0 is indicated in Fig. 3.6. It will be seen that if $r_0 < r_{0,\,crit.}$

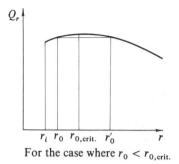

For the case where $r_0 < r_{0,\text{crit.}}$

Fig. 3.6.   Variation of heat loss with thickness of insulation.

the heat loss will be increased by increasing r_0, and that a definite increase in radius, $(r'_0 - r_0)$, is necessary before the heat loss starts to diminish.

In many practical applications the problem does not arise since the tube radius r_i is greater than $r_{0,\text{crit.}}$ (i.e., greater than k/h for the insulating material to be used). The problem can occur particularly if radii are small or the conductivity of the insulating material relatively high and the convection coefficient relatively low.

EXAMPLE 3.2

A small electric heating application uses 15 gauge wire (0·183 cm) with 0·071 cm thick insulation. The thermal conductivity of the insulation is 0·118 W/m deg C, and the surface convection coefficient is 34·1 W/m² deg C. Determine the critical thickness of insulation in this case, and the change in heat transfer rate if the critical thickness was used, assuming the temperature difference between the surface of the wire and surrounding air remains unchanged.

Solution

$$r_{0,\text{crit.}} = \frac{k}{h} = \frac{0·118}{34·1} = 0·00346 \text{ m}$$

$$= 0·346 \text{ cm}$$

The radius of the wire is 0·091 cm, so the critical thickness of insulation is 0·255 cm.

The initial U is given by

$$\frac{1}{U_1} = \frac{1}{2\pi r_0 h} + \frac{\ln r_0/r_i}{2\pi k}$$

$$\therefore \quad \frac{1}{U_1} = \frac{100}{2\pi \times 0.162 \times 34.1} + \frac{\ln 0.162/0.091}{2\pi \times 0.118}$$

$$= 2.88 + 0.78 = 3.66$$

$$\therefore \quad U_1 = 0.273$$

The new U will be given by

$$\frac{1}{U_2} = \frac{100}{2\pi \times 0.346 \times 34.1} + \frac{\ln 0.346/0.091}{2\pi \times 0.118}$$

$$= 1.35 + 1.805 = 3.155$$

$$\therefore \quad U_2 = 0.317$$

Since the initial r_0 was less than $r_{0,\,crit.}$ the heat transfer will be increased by the amount indicated when U_2 is compared with U_1. The increase is $(U_2 - U_1)/U_1 = 0.044/0.273 = 16.1$ per cent.

3.5. Radial Conduction in Spherical Layers

Another simple instance of one-dimensional conduction is that which can occur in a spherical layer. Conduction will be only in the radial direction if the temperatures of the two spherical surfaces are uniform. The radial conduction is given by:

$$Q_r = -4\pi k \frac{r_1 r_2}{r_2 - r_1} . (t_2 - t_1) \qquad (3.20)$$

and the overall heat transfer coefficient for a double spherical layer separating two fluids f_1 and f_2 is

$$1 \bigg/ \left(\frac{1}{4\pi r_1^2 h_{c1}} + \frac{1}{4\pi k_1} . \frac{r_2 - r_1}{r_1 r_2} + \frac{1}{4\pi k_2} . \frac{r_3 - r_2}{r_2 r_3} + \frac{1}{4\pi r_3^2 h_{c2}} \right)$$

The value of the critical r_0 for a sphere is $2k/h$.

3.6. Conduction with Heat Sources

The flow of electricity in a material gives rise to ohmic heating and, generally, the resulting heat flow is at least two-dimensional.

However, if the flow of current in a flat wide bar, or the heating of a flat plate by eddy currents is being considered, then the heat flow is essentially one-dimensional if edge effects are neglected. (See Fig. 3.7, where $l \gg b$).

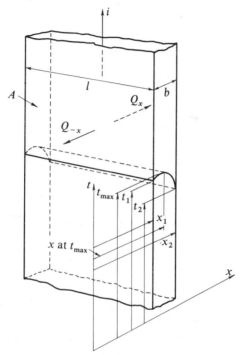

Fig. 3.7. One-dimensional conduction in a plane layer with internal heat generation.

The general equation for the rectangular coordinate system, when applied to this problem, reduces to

$$0 = \alpha\left(\frac{d^2t}{dx^2}\right) + \frac{q'}{\rho c_p} \qquad ((2.10))$$

This equation may be integrated to give

$$t = -\frac{q'x^2}{2k} + C_5 x + C_6 \qquad (3.21)$$

where C_5 and C_6 are constants of integration to be determined from boundary conditions.

The heat transfer at any plane, x, is obtained by differentiating equation (3.21) and applying Fourier's law. Thus

$$q_{x=t} = -k\left(\frac{dt}{dx}\right)_x \qquad (3.22)$$

If $dt/dx = 0$, the temperature is a maximum. This may be found by putting the value of x at which $dt/dx = 0$ into equation (3.21).

One-dimensional conduction in the radial direction will occur in a rod or hollow cylindrical bar if surface temperatures are uniform. The maximum temperature will occur at the centre of a rod, and at an intermediate radius in a hollow bar if both surfaces are cooled.

The general equation in cylindrical coordinates (2.16) reduces to

$$\alpha\left(\frac{d^2t}{dr^2} + \frac{1}{r}\frac{dt}{dr}\right) + \frac{q'}{\rho c_p} = 0 \qquad ((2.17))$$

for this situation. The solution of this is

$$t = -\frac{q'r^2}{4k} + C_7 \ln r + C_8 \qquad (3.23)$$

which may be obtained by making the substitution $dt/dr = p$. Values of C_7 and C_8, the constants of integration, may be found by substituting the known boundary conditions, see Fig. 3.8. The value of r at which $dt/dr = 0$ gives the position of the maximum temperature, and this substituted in (3.23) gives the value of the maximum temperature.

The following example illustrates the way in which ohmic heating problems may be solved.

EXAMPLE 3.3

An internally cooled copper conductor of 4 cm outer diameter and 1·5 cm inner diameter carries a current density of 5000 amp/cm². The temperature of the inner surface is maintained at 70°C, and it may be assumed that no heat transfer takes place through insulation surrounding the copper. Determine the equation for temperature distribution through the copper, hence find the maximum temperature of the copper, the radius at which it occurs, and the heat transfer rate internally. Check that this is equal to the total energy generation in the conductor. For copper, take $k = 380$ W/m deg C and the resistivity $\rho = 2 \times 10^{-8}$ ohm metre.

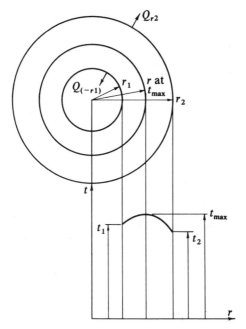

Fig. 3.8.   Radial conduction in a cylindrical layer with internal heat generation.

Solution. If i is the current density,

$$q' = \rho i^2 = 2 \times 10^{-8} \times (5000 \times 10^4)^2 \text{ W/m}^3$$

$$= 5 \times 10^7 \text{ W/m}^3$$

The boundary conditions are that at $r = 0.75$ cm, $t = 70°$C and that at $r = 2$ cm, $dt/dr = 0$. This is because the heat transfer is zero at $r = 2$ cm. It follows that the maximum temperature also occurs at $r = 2$ cm. The constants of integration in equation (3.23) may now be found.

$$\frac{dt}{dr} = -\frac{q'r}{2k} + \frac{C_7}{r} = 0 \qquad \text{at} \qquad r = 0.02$$

$$\therefore \quad -\frac{5 \times 10^7 \times 0.02}{2 \times 380} + \frac{C_7}{0.02} = 0$$

$$\therefore \quad -1318 + C_7/0.02 = 0$$

$$C_7 = 26.3$$

C_8 is given by

$$70 = -\frac{5 \times 10^7}{4 \times 380} \times \left(\frac{0.75}{100}\right)^2 + 26.3 \ln (0.0075) + C_8$$

$$= -1.85 - 128.7 + C_8$$

$$\therefore \quad C_8 = 200.6$$

The equation for temperature is therefore:

$$t = -32,900r^2 + 26.3 \ln r + 200.6$$

with r in metres.

The maximum temperature occurs at the outer radius. Substituting $r = 0.02$ m in the above equation gives

$$t_{max} = -13.17 - 102.8 + 200.6$$

$$= 84.6°C$$

To calculate the heat transfer rate internally, it is first necessary to find the temperature gradient at $r = 0.0075$ m. Thus

$$\left(\frac{dt}{dr}\right)_{r=0.0075} = -\frac{5 \times 10^7 \times 0.0075}{2 \times 380} + \frac{26.3}{0.0075}$$

$$= -494 + 3510$$

$$= +3016$$

The heat transfer internally is in the direction of negative radius, hence

$$Q_{(-r)} = -\left(-kA\frac{dt}{dr}\right)$$

$$= +380 \times (2\pi \times 0.0075) \times 3016$$

$$= 53,900 \text{ W/m length}$$

This result may be checked since all the heat generated in the conductor must be dissipated internally.

$$\therefore \quad Q_{(-r)} = (\text{volume/m length}) \times q'$$

$$= \pi(0.02^2 - 0.0075^2) \times 5 \times 10^7$$

$$= 53,900 \text{ W/m length.}$$

PROBLEMS

1. The walls of a refrigerator for a shop consist of slag wool 0·1522 m thick sandwiched between sheet iron, 0·0794 cm thick, on one side and asbestos board, 0·953 cm thick, on the other. The total surface effective for heat transfer is 37·2 m². The atmospheric temperature is 18·3°C and the temperature in the cold room is −3·9°C.

The thermal conductivity of iron, slag wool, and asbestos board may be taken as 69·1, 0·346 and 1·21 respectively and the surface heat transfer coefficient as 1·705; all in J s m °C, units.

Compute the heat leakage into the refrigerator. (Ans. 510 W.) (*King's College, London*).

2. A spherical container 1·22 m internal diameter is made of sheet metal of negligible thermal resistance and covered by cork insulation 0·457 m thick. The interior contains a liquefied gas at −62·2°C for which a surface heat transfer coefficient of 1060 J/m² s deg C may be considered to apply. The atmospheric temperature is 18·3°C. Moisture vapour permeates the cork and freezes at a suitable position to form an ice barrier. The mean surface coefficient for the outside may be regarded as 21 J/m² s deg. Calculate the thickness of the ice assuming that the conduction characteristics of the cork remain constant throughout.

Assume the thermal conductivity for cork is 0·0432 J/m s deg C. (Ans. 0·305 m.) *Queen Mary College, London*).

3. Steam at 200 lbf/in.² flows through a pipe 2 in. O.D. and 150 ft long. The pipe is covered by a 1 in. thick layer of lagging of conductivity 0·08 Btu/ft h deg F. When the steam enters the pipe dry saturated at a rate of 370 lb/h and the surrounding air temperature is 70°F, the film coefficient of heat transfer for the outer surface of the lagging is 0·8 Btu/ft² h deg F. It may be assumed that there is no appreciable temperature drop between the steam and the outer surface of the pipe.

Derive an expression for the heat loss per foot run of pipe and calculate the dryness of the steam at outlet from the pipe and the outside temperature of the lagging. (Ans. 0·94, 215°F.) (*University College, London*).

4. Explain the analogy between heat transfer by conduction and the conduction of electricity through ohmic resistances, using the composite wall of a building as an illustration.

An electrical cable comprises a wire of 0·05 in. diameter enclosed by an insulating sheath 0·1 in. thick. The thermal conductivity of the insulating material is 0·10 Btu/ft h deg F. The cable is suspended in still air at 60°F. The heat transfer coefficient h between the air and the outer surface of the insulator is not constant, but depends on the temperature difference, $T_{surface} - T_{air}$, expressed in °F, in accordance with the equation:

$$h = 0·4 (T_{surface} - T_{air})^{\frac{1}{4}} \text{ Btu/ft}^2 \text{ h deg F}$$

If no part of the insulating material is to exceed a temperature of 300°F, determine, to two significant figures and in Btu/ft h, the maximum 'I^2R losses' which can be permitted in the wire. (Hint: Trial-and-error is needed.) (Ans. 19 Btu/ft h.) (*Imperial College, London*).

5. (i) Define the term thermal resistance and show that, when heat flows through a number of individual resistances in series, the overall resistance is equal to the sum of the individual resistances.

(ii) A double-glazed window consists of two sheets of glass separated by a gap. The gap is filled with a gas, but is sufficiently thin to prevent convection between the two sheets of glass. The area of the window in elevation is A, the thickness of each sheet of glass is x and the thickness of the gap is y. The thermal conductivities of the glass and of the gas in the gap are k_x and k_y respectively. The surface heat-transfer coefficients inside and outside the building are h_1 and h_2 respectively; the corresponding air temperatures are t_1 and t_2. Neglecting radiation, obtain an expression for the heat transfer rate q, in terms of A, x, y, k_x, k_y, h_1, h_2, t_1, and t_2.

(iii) Find the percentage reduction in heat loss when a single-glazed window is replaced by a double-glazed window. Assume that the values of A, x, k_x, h_1, h_2, t_1, and t_2 are the same for both windows, the symbols having the same meaning as in section (ii). Numerical data:

$x = 0.318$ cm; $\qquad\qquad y = 0.635$ cm;
$k_x = 0.865$ J/m s deg C; $\qquad k_y = 0.026$ J/m s deg C;
$h_1 = 8.52$ J/m^2 s deg C; $\qquad h_2 = 14.2$ J/m^2 s deg C.
(Ans. 56·5 per cent) $\qquad\qquad\qquad\qquad$ (*Imperial College, London*).

6. It is proposed to insulate a copper pipe of 0·5 in. inside diameter and wall thickness 0·0625 in. with a surrounding cylinder of insulation material having a thermal conductivity 0·2 Btu/h ft^2(deg F/ft). Perfect contact between the insulation and the pipe surface may be assumed. The pipe carries water at 160°F and heat is lost to air at 40°F, the surface heat transfer coefficients being 200 Btu/h ft^2 deg F and 2 Btu/h ft^2 deg F on the inside and outside surfaces respectively. The thermal conductivity of copper is 220 Btu/h ft^2 (deg F/ft).

(a) Show that the rate of heat loss will be a maximum when the outside radius of the insulation is 1·2 in.,

(b) determine the outside diameter of the insulation when the rate of heat loss is equal to that for the uninsulated pipe, and

(c) calculate the temperatures at the inner and outer surfaces of the insulation for the conditions of case (b).

Temperatures may be assumed to be steady and heat flow to be radial. (Ans. 26 in., 158°F, 42·9°F.) (*University College, London*).

7. Show that for the conduction of heat in an isotropic solid, the following equation holds:

$$\frac{\partial}{\partial x}k\frac{\partial T}{\partial x} + \frac{\partial}{\partial y}k\frac{\partial T}{\partial y} + \frac{\partial}{\partial z}k\frac{\partial T}{\partial z} + Q''' = \rho c\frac{\partial T}{\partial t}$$

where T, k, ρ, c, and Q''' are temperature, thermal conductivity, density, specific heat-capacity, and density of rate of heat supply respectively; and where t is the time and x, y, z are rectangular cartesian coordinates.

A thin ribbon of metal carries an electric current of density J and is immersed in an electrically non-conducting liquid which is thereby caused to boil and is at a uniform temperature. The heat transfer coefficient between the ribbon and the liquid is also uniform. Show that the mean temperature of the ribbon (as estimated, for example by resistance measurements) exceeds the surface temperature by:

$$J^2 \sigma b^2 / 3k$$

where $2b$ and σ are the thickness and the electrical resistivity of the ribbon. (Assume that J, σ, and k are uniform and that the loss from the edges is negligible.) (*Queen Mary College, London*).

8. Show that the heat transferred in steady conduction through a hollow sphere is given by

$$Q = \frac{4\pi k r r_1}{r - r_1}(t_1 - t)$$

where r and r_1, t and t_1 are the outer and inner radii and temperatures respectively.

A thin sphere of radius r_1 is maintained at a temperature t_1 by internal heating, in surroundings at t_2. The sphere is covered with an 'insulating' layer of conductivity k and radius r. Give a physical explanation for the fact that a certain thickness of insulation may increase the rate of heat loss rather than reduce it; prove that for maximum heat loss $r = 2k/h$, where h is the heat transfer coefficient based on unit area of outer surface. (*University of Bristol*).

9. An electric current carrying cable has a solid core of radius r_1, covered by an outer concentric layer of insulation to radius r_2. Resistance heating, assumed homogeneous, is Q Btu per sec per ft length. The insulation material has a thermal conductivity k Btu/ft s deg F and surface heat transfer coefficient h Btu/ft^2 s deg F.

Show that the steady temperature on the core surface, relative to the surroundings is

$$\frac{Q}{2\pi}\left(\frac{1}{k}\log_e \frac{r_2}{r_1} + \frac{1}{r_2 h}\right) °F$$

Hence establish that a choice of outer radius $r_2 = k/h$ yields the minimum core surface temperature.

Show that the temperature distribution within the core is given by

$$\frac{Q}{\pi r_1^2 k_c} = \frac{d^2 t}{dr^2} + \frac{1}{r}\frac{dt}{dr}$$

where t is the temperature at radius r and k_c is the thermal conductivity of the core.

A solution of the equation

$$A = \frac{d^2 y}{dx^2} + \frac{1}{x}\frac{dy}{dx}$$

may be taken as $y = \frac{1}{4}Ax^2 + c$.

Establish that, for the condition of minimum temperature, the temperature at the cable axis, above the surroundings is

$$\frac{Q}{2\pi}\left(\frac{1}{k}\log_e\frac{k}{r_1 h} + \frac{1}{k} + \frac{1}{2k_c}\right)$$

(*University of Glasgow*).

10. Heat is generated at a uniform rate q in each unit of volume of a plate of large surface area and of thickness L. The faces of the plate are cooled so that their temperatures are maintained at θ_1 and θ_2 in a region remote from the edges. The thermal conductivity k of the plate material is constant.

Show that the maximum temperature within the plate is

$$\frac{\theta_1 + \theta_2}{2} + \frac{qL^2}{8k} + \frac{k}{2qL^2}\left(\theta_2 - \theta_1\right)^2 \qquad (\textit{University of Manchester}).$$

4

Two-dimensional steady state conduction

It is important to realize that in many cases a conduction problem is over simplified by the use of one-dimensional treatment, which means the neglect of edge and corner effects which must be present in any finite object. The error involved in this neglect will depend on the dimensions of the system. Consider, for example, the wall of a building some 20 ft long and 9 in. thick. In the absence of doors and windows, conduction through such a wall will be one-dimensional over the greater part of the 20 ft length and the error involved in neglecting the corner effects will not be great. In contrast, conduction through a chimney, say, 9 in. square internally and 27 in. square externally, is *essentially* two-dimensional. Again a simplifying assumption is being made, since near the base and top of the chimney conduction will be three-dimensional. Thus those problems will be considered in this chapter which may be assumed to be two-dimensional without introducing error. This will cover the majority of heat conduction problems which are sufficiently simple to include in an introductory text.

Two-dimensional problems in rectangular coordinates only are to be considered. The two equations, with and without heat generation, are:

$$\alpha\left(\frac{\partial^2 t}{\partial x^2} + \frac{\partial^2 t}{\partial y^2}\right) + \frac{q'}{\rho c_{\mathrm{p}}} = 0 \qquad ((2.9))$$

$$\frac{\partial^2 t}{\partial x^2} + \frac{\partial^2 t}{\partial y^2} = 0 \qquad ((2.11))$$

Solutions to these equations are, of course, possible, but the more readily obtained ones depend on the choice of somewhat unrepresentative configurations or boundary conditions. As an alternative,

39

therefore, an approximate numerical method will be described. This has the advantage that it is applicable to any two-dimensional shape regardless of its complexity or the boundary condition. The exactness obtained by difficult analytical solution is hardly justified when it is remembered that the problem may only be an approximation to two-dimensional conduction.

The main difference between the analytical solution and the numerical method is that the former will give an equation from which the temperature may be obtained anywhere in the solid, whereas the latter will give values of temperature at chosen specific points only. The accuracy will depend on how close together are the chosen points; however, many points will entail much more work than a few.

4.1. A Numerical Solution of Two-Dimensional Conduction

The numerical method[1] will first be described in conjunction with a typical example of two-dimensional conduction, the right-angled corner. Then, a second example will be given involving conduction in a bus bar, which carries an electric current.

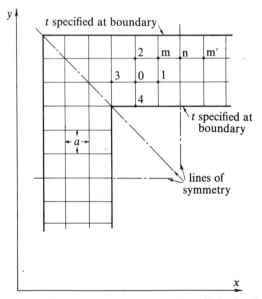

Fig. 4.1. Construction for a numerical solution of two-dimensional conduction, in a quarter of a hollow square section.

The right-angled corner to be discussed is shown in Fig. 4.1. A plan of the corner is first drawn, then a square mesh is super-imposed. It is assumed that the corner forms a part of a square hollow section, such as a chimney. Therefore, if the two boundary temperatures are uniform on the inside and outside surfaces, conduction will be symmetrical and only half of one corner of the chimney need be considered.

The first objective is to determine the temperatures at all the mesh points. To do this a guess is made of likely values, bearing in mind the boundary temperatures and the positions of mesh points in relation to the boundaries. Then, by a process of *relaxation*, the correct values are derived from the guessed values. The amount of numerical work involved at this stage will be reduced if the initial guesses are quite close to the actual values.

In order to examine the numerical process, consider any mesh point and the four points immediately surrounding it. Let a be the distance between points. Thus the coordinates of the five points 0 to 4 in Fig. 4.1 are

$$
\begin{array}{llll}
\text{point 0,} & x = 0, & y = 0 \\
\text{point 1,} & x = a, & y = 0 \\
\text{point 2,} & x = 0, & y = a \\
\text{point 3,} & x = -a, & y = 0 \\
\text{point 4,} & x = 0, & y = -a
\end{array}
$$

As the temperature varies continuously in the x- and y-directions within the field, the temperature distributions in the x- and y-directions through point 0 may each be written as a power series, thus

$$t = m_0 + m_1 x + m_2 x^2 + m_3 x^3 + \dots \qquad \text{at} \quad y = 0$$

$$t = n_0 + n_1 y + n_2 y^2 + n_3 y^3 + \dots \qquad \text{at} \quad x = 0$$

Next, using a MacLaurin's series, it is possible to express the temperature variations in the x- and y-directions in terms of the differential coefficients of $t = f(x)$ and $t = g(y)$ at $x = 0$, and $y = 0$. Thus:

$$t = t_0 + \left(\frac{\partial t}{\partial x}\right)_0 \frac{x}{1!} + \left(\frac{\partial^2 t}{\partial x^2}\right) \frac{x^2}{2!} + \left(\frac{\partial^3 t}{\partial x^3}\right) \frac{x^3}{3!} + \dots \qquad \text{at} \quad y = 0 \quad (4.1)$$

$$t = t_0 + \left(\frac{\partial t}{\partial y}\right)_0 \frac{y}{1!} + \left(\frac{\partial^2 t}{\partial y^2}\right) \frac{y^2}{2!} + \left(\frac{\partial^3 t}{\partial y^3}\right) \frac{y^3}{3!} + \dots \qquad \text{at} \quad x = 0 \quad (4.2)$$

Using equations (4.1) and (4.2) and the chosen increment, it is now possible to write down to the required degree of accuracy the temperatures at points 1 to 4 in terms of t_0 and the differential coefficients. For example,

$$\text{at} \quad x = a, \quad t_1 = t_0 + \left(\frac{\partial t}{\partial x}\right)_0 a + \left(\frac{\partial^2 t}{\partial x^2}\right)_0 \frac{a^2}{2} + \left(\frac{\partial^3 t}{\partial x^3}\right)_0 \frac{a^3}{6} \tag{4.3}$$

$$\text{at} \quad x = -a, \quad t_3 = t_0 - \left(\frac{\partial t}{\partial x}\right)_0 a + \left(\frac{\partial^2 t}{\partial x^2}\right)_0 \frac{a^2}{2} - \left(\frac{\partial^3 t}{\partial x^3}\right)_0 \frac{a^3}{6} \tag{4.4}$$

neglecting higher powers. Equations (4.3) and (4.4) when added give

$$t_1 + t_3 = 2t_0 + \left(\frac{\partial^2 t}{\partial x^2}\right)_0 a^2 \tag{4.5}$$

In a similar manner it is possible to obtain

$$t_2 + t_4 = 2t_0 + \left(\frac{\partial^2 t}{\partial y^2}\right)_0 a^2 \tag{4.6}$$

Re-arranging equations (4.5) and (4.6) gives

$$\left(\frac{\partial^2 t}{\partial x^2}\right)_0 = \frac{t_1 + t_3 - 2t_0}{a^2} \tag{4.7}$$

and

$$\left(\frac{\partial^2 t}{\partial y^2}\right)_0 = \frac{t_2 + t_4 - 2t_0}{a^2} \tag{4.8}$$

and the sum of equations (4.7) and (4.8) gives a solution of equation (2.11), accurate to the order of equations (4.3) and (4.4). Thus

$$\left(\frac{\partial^2 t}{\partial x^2}\right)_0 + \left(\frac{\partial^2 t}{\partial y^2}\right)_0 = \frac{t_1 + t_2 + t_3 + t_4 - 4t_0}{a^2} = 0 \tag{4.9}$$

If there is heat generation within the material, equation (2.9) may be re-written as

$$\frac{\partial^2 t}{\partial x^2} + \frac{\partial^2 t}{\partial y^2} + \frac{q'}{k} = 0 \tag{4.10}$$

and a solution of this written as:

$$\frac{t_1 + t_2 + t_3 + t_4 - 4t_0}{a^2} + \frac{q'}{k} = 0 \tag{4.11}$$

The finite difference relationships, equations (4.9) and (4.11), relate the temperatures at point 0 to the temperatures at the four surrounding points. Obviously, similar equations may be written for other points and, in fact, there will be as many equations as there are mesh points. The task is then to obtain simultaneous solutions to all the equations. However, to avoid the labour involved in doing this, the guessed values of temperature are used in the finite difference relationships, and these values are gradually adjusted in the relaxation procedure until the correct solution of all finite difference relationships is obtained. When the original guessed temperatures are substituted, residuals are generally obtained. For example, suppose $t_0 = 100°$, $t_1 = 105°$, $t_2 = 70°$, $t_3 = 79°$, $t_4 = 150°$. On substituting in equation (4.9), a residual of $+4$ at point 0 is obtained, since from equation (4.9) it is clear that $t_1 + t_2 + t_3 + t_4 - 4t_0 = 0$. In a similar manner various other residual values may be obtained at other points. The object is to reduce all residuals to zero. The simplest way of eliminating the residual at point 0 is to increase t_0 by $1°$. This is obvious on inspection of equation (4.9). Thus to eliminate a residual of $+r$, the temperature at the point must be altered by $+\frac{1}{4}r$; to eliminate a residual of $-r$, the temperature must be altered by $-\frac{1}{4}r$. The residuals of surrounding points will change by the same amount as the change to t_0 itself, i.e., $\pm\frac{1}{4}r$. These facts are summarized for convenience in Fig. 4.2. As point 4 is on the boundary, t_4 is specified and will not change. There is therefore no residual at 4 to be altered, in this particular example.

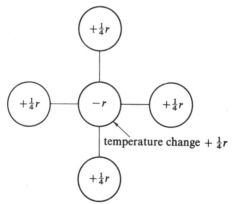

Fig. 4.2. Effect on the residuals of changing the temperature at a point by $+\frac{1}{4}r$.

A further detail to note concerns points in the vicinity of lines of symmetry, as for example points m, n, and m′ in Fig. 4.1. n lies on a line of symmetry, and consequently m and m′ have the same temperature. If, to eliminate a residual at m, t_m is changed by $+\frac{1}{4}r$, then $t_{m'}$ must also be changed by $+\frac{1}{4}r$, and the residual at n will consequently change by $\frac{2}{4}r$. On the other hand, if t_n is changed by $\frac{1}{4}r$, the residuals at m and m′ will change by the same amount, $\frac{1}{4}r$.

If a problem with heat generation is being solved, then equation (4.11) shows that

$$t_1 + t_2 + t_3 + t_4 - 4t_0 = -\frac{a^2 q'}{k}$$

i.e., the residual must then be $-a^2 q'/k$ instead of 0.

All residuals, then, are gradually reduced in the manner indicated, the largest residuals being eliminated first. Subsequent relaxations often produce a new residual at a point previously dealt with, and it is not unusual for the same point to be relaxed several times. The process is generally stopped when residuals are ± 2 or less; this avoids fractional temperatures in the final solution.

Having completed the relaxation, the second objective is to determine the heat flow. To do this, consider again the five points 0 to 4 in Fig. 4.1, shown again in Fig. 4.3, each point now being at

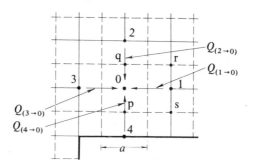

Fig. 4.3.   Conduction between mesh points.

the centre of a square of side a. Heat transfer is assumed to occur only along the mesh lines, thus the heat transfer to point 0 from point 1 is along the line 1–0, and its magnitude is calculated assuming line rs is everywhere at t_1 and pq is everywhere at t_0. Thus, for unit depth of material,

$$Q_{(1 \text{ to } 0)} = \frac{-k(a \times 1)(t_0 - t_1)}{a} = k(t_1 - t_0)$$

Similarly, the heat transfer from points 2, 3, and 4 to 0 are $k(t_2 - t_0)$, $k(t_3 - t_0)$, and $k(t_4 - t_0)$, respectively. Hence the total heat transfer towards point 0 is

$$\sum Q = k(t_1 + t_2 + t_3 + t_4 - 4t_0) \tag{4.12}$$

It will be obvious that greatest accuracy will be obtained in this calculation for the smallest mesh size a, with the corresponding closeness in values of temperature at the five points. In steady state, and in the absence of internal heat generation, the nett sum of heat transfer towards point 0, (4.12), must be zero since otherwise t_0 would change with time. Consequently, $t_1 + t_2 + t_3 + t_4 - 4t_0 = 0$. Further, if there is uniform heat generation, the nett sum of heat transfer towards point 0 will be the negative of the heat generation in unit depth of the square of side a surrounding point 0.

$$\therefore \qquad k(t_1 + t_2 + t_3 + t_4 - 4t_0) = -q'a^2$$

$$\therefore \qquad \frac{t_1 + t_2 + t_3 + t_4 - 4t_0}{a^2} + \frac{q'}{k} = 0 \qquad ((4.11))$$

Thus the finite difference relationship (4.11) (and from which (4.9) follows), has been derived via what is sometimes called the conducting rod analogy.

The total heat flow into and out of two-dimensional shapes may be calculated by considering only the 'rods', i.e., mesh lines, that terminate at boundary points.

This procedure may also be used at a surface in conjunction with a fixed fluid temperature and a convection coefficient h. In this case the temperature at the solid surface is no longer the fixed boundary condition. The method is given in Ref. 2. In Fig. 4.4, t_f is the fluid

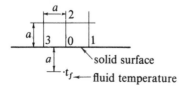

Fig. 4.4.   Relaxation network at a solid surface/fluid interface.

temperature at an assumed mesh point in the fluid at distance a from point 0 on the surface. The heat transfer from points 1, 2, and 3 to point 0 by conduction will be $k(t_1 - t_0) + k(t_2 - t_0) + k(t_3 - t_0)$. The heat transfer from the point in the fluid, point 4, by convection will be $ha(t_f - t_0)$. Thus, the total heat transfer to point 0 is

$$k\left[t_1 + t_2 + t_3 + \frac{hat_f}{k} - t_0\left(3 + \frac{ha}{k}\right)\right]$$

If t_4 is substituted for $\dfrac{hat_f}{k} + t_0\left(1 - \dfrac{ha}{k}\right)$, t_4 can be regarded as a fixed boundary temperature at an imaginary solid surface distance a beyond the real one. The relaxation may then proceed in the normal way, and the real solid boundary temperatures will be found.

EXAMPLE 4.1

A 2 ft square brick chimney has walls 6 in. thick and a 1 ft square cavity. The inside surface temperature is 300°F and the outside surface temperature 60°F. Using a 2 in. mesh, determine the temperature distribution within the brick, and the rate of heat transfer, per ft height of chimney. k for the brick is 0·4 Btu/ft h deg F.

Solution. Figure 4.5 shows a quarter of the section. Only half of this need be considered. Mesh points are identified by letters a to l. Original guessed values of temperature are shown to the left of the points, final values obtained by relaxation are to the right, and underlined. The relaxation sequence may be followed in Table 4.1. The initial residuals are first calculated, and then the residuals are reduced, working with the largest first. The final residuals are ± 2 or smaller, and their sum is zero, so that on average the relaxation is complete.

Next, the heat transfer may be calculated using the conducting rod analogy. Heat transfer to the brick is given by

$$4k[(300 - 217) + 2(300 - 216) + 2(300 - 211) + 2(300 - 196)]$$

$$= 4k(83 + 168 + 178 + 208) = 2548k$$

Heat transfer from the brick is

$$4k[(137 - 60) + 2(136 - 60) + 2(132 - 60) + 2(122 - 60)$$

$$+ 2(104 - 60) + 2(82 - 60)]$$

$$= 4k(77 + 152 + 144 + 124 + 88 + 44) = 2516k$$

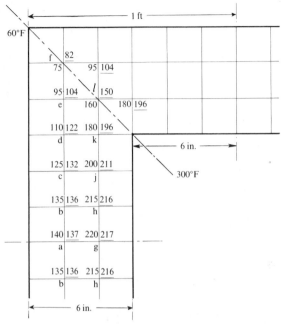

Fig. 4.5. *Boundary conditions, initial and final temperatures for Example 4.1.*

The agreement here is reasonable considering the size of the mesh. The average value may be used. Hence the heat transfer per ft height of chimney is $2532k$ or 1013 Btu/ft.

EXAMPLE 4.2

An alloy bus bar is of right-angled section $5\frac{1}{2}$ cm by $5\frac{1}{2}$ cm by 1 cm thick. It carries a current of 27,700 amps. It is air cooled. The surface temperatures are as indicated in Fig. 4.6. Using a mesh size of 0·5 cm square, determine the temperature distribution in the cross-section. Calculate also the energy dissipated per metre length. For the alloy, the thermal conductivity is 76·6 watt/m deg C, and the resistivity is 4×10^{-8} ohm m.

Solution. The area of cross-section is 10 cm². Hence the current density is 2770 amp/cm².

$$\therefore \quad q' = \rho i^2 = (4 \times 10^{-8})\,\text{ohm m} \times (2770 \times 10^4)^2(\text{amp/m}^2)^2$$
$$= 30\cdot7 \times 10^6 \text{ watt/m}^3$$

Table 4.1

Mesh point		a	b	c	d	e	f	g	h	j	k	l
Initial temp (°F)		140	135	125	110	95	75	220	215	200	180	160
Initial residual		−10	0	5	20	25	10	−10	−5	20	50	−90
Operation	**New temp. (°F)**											
−22 at l	138					3					28	−2
+7 k	187				27					27	0	12
+7 j	207			12					2	−1	7	
+7 d	117			19	−1	10					14	
+5 c	130		5	−1	4					4		
+4 k	191				8					8	−2	20
+5 l	143					15					3	0
+4 e	99				12	−1	18					8
+5 f	80					4	−2					
+3 d	120			2	0	7					6	
−2 a	138	−2	3					−12				
−3 g	217	−5						0	−1			
+2 j	209			4					1	0	8	
+2 k	193				2					2	0	12
+3 l	146					10					3	0
+3 e	102				−2		4					6
+1 l	147					−1					4	2
+1 f	81					0	0					
+1 k	194				3					3	0	4
+1 l	148					1					1	0
+1 j	210			5					2	−1	2	
+1 c	131		4	1	4					0		
−1 a	137	−1	3					−1				
+1 d	121			2	0	2					3	
+1 b	136	1	−1	3					3			
+1 c	132		0	−1	1					1		
+1 h	216		1					1	−1	2		
+1 k	195				2					3	−1	2
+1 j	211		0						0	−1	0	
+1 e	103				−2		2					4
+1 l	149					−1					1	0
+1 f	82					0	−2					
+1 d	122			1	−2	1					2	
+1 k	196				−1					0	−2	2
+1 l	150					2				−1	−2	
+1 e	104				−2		0					
Final temp. (°F)		137	136	132	122	104	82	217	216	211	196	150

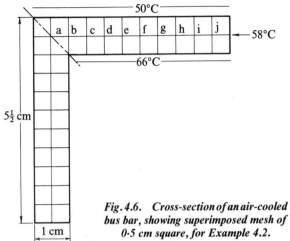

Fig. 4.6. Cross-section of an air-cooled bus bar, showing superimposed mesh of 0·5 cm square, for Example 4.2.

In the relaxation procedure, the residual is $-a^2q'/k$

$$a^2q'/k = \frac{(0\cdot005)^2\,\text{m}^2 \times (30\cdot7 \times 10^6)\,\text{watt/m}^3}{76\cdot6\,\text{watt/m deg C}} = 10\,\text{deg C}$$

Hence the residual must be -10.

Referring to the figure, it can be assumed that conduction is one-dimensional in the region of points d–h. Applying equation (4.11) to these points it will be found that their temperature is 63°. The initial values of temperature for all points a–j are given, as assumed, in Table 4.2. The subsequent solution follows.

Table 4.2

Point	a	b	c	d	e	f	g	h	i	j
Initial temp. (°C)	63	63	63	63	63	63	63	63	62	60
Initial residual	−26	−10	−10	−10	−10	−10	−10	−11	−9	−4
Operation										
−4° at a, a = 59°	−10	−14								
−1° at b, b = 62°	−12	−10	−11							
−½° at a, a = 58½°	−10	−10½								
+1½° at j, j = 61½°									−7½	−10
+½° at i, i = 62½°								−10½	−9½	−9½
Final temp. (°C)	58½	62	63	63	63	63	63	63	62½	61½

The energy dissipated may be calculated directly from the electrical loading of the bar.

The volume per metre length is $10\,\text{cm}^2 \times 100\,\text{cm} = 1000\,\text{cm}^3$. The energy dissipated is thus $30\cdot7 \times 1000\,\text{watt/m} = 30\cdot7\,\text{kW/m}$. This wasted energy results directly from the high resistivity of this particular material.

4.2. An Electrical Analogy of Two-Dimensional Conduction

The similarity between the conduction of heat due to a temperature difference and the conduction of electricity due to a potential difference has already been mentioned. It will now be seen that this makes possible a useful analogy technique, to simulate two-dimensional heat conduction by electrical means. Unit thickness or depth of the heat conducting system is replaced by a model in an electrically conducting medium. Conducting paper is often used, which may be only a few thousandths of an inch thick compared with, say, a foot of the thermal system. Potentials applied to the boundaries of the paper model represent the temperatures and the total current flowing is equivalent to the total heat flow. It is thus possible to determine, from a simple experiment and without using lengthy numerical procedure, the heat flow in a complex geometrical system. In addition, constant potential lines, which are analogous to isothermal lines, may readily be plotted using a potentiometer.

The general arrangement of a conducting paper experiment is shown in Fig. 4.7a. The limits of the two-dimensional shape on the conducting paper are bounded by lines painted on the paper using a conducting silver paint. A painted line has two edges, and it is important that the correct edge of each line conforms exactly to the limit of the model shape. It will be appreciated that it is only feasible to simulate the simpler type of problem involving a uniform temperature difference between boundaries. It is therefore important to ensure that the potential difference is, in fact, uniform between two painted lines, and to avoid local spots of high resistance in the paint it is advisable to bury a copper wire within the painted line. The model must, of course, be geometrically similar to the actual problem, but the actual size does not matter. The only measurements necessary to solve any conducting problem are the potential difference and the current. It is instructive to plot constant potential lines as well; these should preferably be equally spaced, i.e., at intervals of, say, 10 or 25 per cent of the total potential difference.

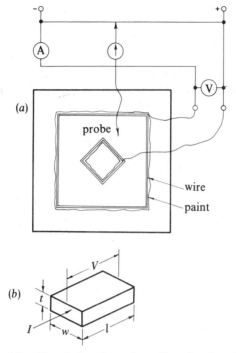

Fig. 4.7.   Electrical analogy of two-dimensional conduction.

An element of conducting paper, length l, width w, and thickness t, is shown in Fig. 4.7b. There is a potential difference of V between the ends of the length l, and a current I is flowing.

If R is the resistance of the element, then

$$I = \frac{V}{R}$$

and $R = \rho l / wt$, where ρ is the resistivity of the material; (units of ohms × length).

Then,

$$I = \frac{wt}{\rho l} V$$

$$= S_i \frac{t}{\rho} V \qquad (4.13)$$

where S_i is the 'shape factor'. The shape factor for this rectangular element is w/l. Any other geometrical shape which passed the same current for the same voltage drop would have the same shape factor.

A similar equation may now be written for a geometrically similar element, length L, width W and thickness T, along which heat is conducting. θ is the temperature difference and k the conductivity, hence from Fourier's law,

$$Q = k\frac{WT}{L}\theta$$

$$= kS_q T\theta \tag{4.14}$$

where $S_q = W/L$ and is the shape factor for the element. As the elements are geometrically similar, the shape factors are equal. Dividing (4.14) by (4.13):

$$\frac{Q}{I} = \frac{kT}{t/\rho}\frac{\theta}{V}$$

$$\therefore \quad Q = I\left(\frac{\rho}{t}\right)k\frac{\theta}{V} \tag{4.15}$$

Q will be in heat units per unit length and time, with T as unit thickness. Thus from measurements of I and V and from a knowledge of θ and k for the conducting problem, the heat flow may be calculated. Equation (4.15) is valid for any geometrical shape, provided the prototype and model are geometrically similar, when the shape factors are equal. ρ/t is a property of the conducting paper and is supplied by the manufacturers. It has a value of about 2000 ohms per square. ($R = \rho l/wt = \rho/t$ for a square, regardless of its size.)

Problems

1. A long oven 4 ft by 6 ft in section is surrounded by a 2 ft thickness of masonry having a coefficient of conductivity of 0·5 in. ft lb °F hour units. The figure shows one quarter of the section. The inner surface of the masonry is at 600°F and the outer at 200°F.

The temperatures (°F) at a series of points at 1 ft centres are approximately:

A	B	C	D	E	F	G	H
400	398	380	300	380	390	398	400

Relax each value once and use the values so obtained to find the rate of flow of heat from AB–H to the outer face of the masonry per ft length of oven. (Ans. 2425 Btu/ft.) (*University College, London*).

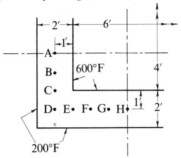

2. The sketch below represents a cross-section of a homogeneous bar of metal, the faces of the bar being maintained at the temperature shown. Show how the relaxation method of obtaining the temperatures at the points A, B, C, D, E, and F is derived, and use the method to make a first estimate of these temperatures, working to the nearest degree.

(Note. Rigorous derivation is not required, merely description and the important assumptions.) (Ans. A, C, 79°; B, 81°, D, F, 52°; E, 50°.) (*University of Leeds*).

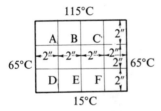

3. A small brick furnace is 30 in. square and has a square interior as shown. The inside surface temperature is 1200°F. The outside surface convects to the atmosphere at 70°F, the convection coefficient being 2·12 Btu/ft² h deg F. Neglecting end effects calculate the hourly heat loss per foot length. Use a 3 in. grid. k for the brick is 0·53 Btu/ft h deg F. (Ans. 4150 Btu/ft h.)

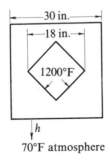

4. An H-section copper conductor (see diagram) carries an overload current of 54,000 amps. In steady state conditions, the surface temperature is 60°C. Using a 0·5 cm grid, determine the temperatures within the copper. Calculate the heat transfer rate at the surface, watt/cm length. The electrical resistivity of copper is 2×10^{-8} ohm m, and the thermal conductivity is 381 watt/m deg C. (Ans. 730 W/cm.)

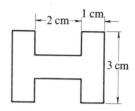

REFERENCES

1. Dusinberre, G. M. *Heat Transfer Calculations by Finite Differences*, International Text-book Company, Scranton, (1961).
2. Jakob, M. *Heat Transfer*, Vol. 1, John Wiley and Sons (1949).

5

One-dimensional transient conduction

In any thermal system, transient heat transfer generally occurs before and after steady state operating conditions. The time duration of the transient condition is of importance in design. A simple approach to this problem is to assume a uniform temperature of the system at any given time. A more detailed approach and other examples of transient heat transfer, e.g., heat treatment processes, require a knowledge of the variation of temperature in the system.

5.1. The Uniform Temperature System

As an example, consider an electric motor. When it is switched on, a uniform rate of waste heat generation commences. The resulting rise in temperature is assumed uniform throughout the machine. This rise in temperature is checked by the cooling rate, which is a function of the temperature rise, and equilibrium is achieved when the rate of cooling is equal to the rate of heat generation. A numerical example will illustrate the approach.

EXAMPLE 5.1

A field coil has a surface area of $0.12\,\text{m}^2$, a mean specific heat of 350 J/kg deg C, and a mass of 20 kg. It dissipates 250 W. The surface convection coefficient is 40 W/m^2 deg C. Calculate the final steady temperature rise and the time constant.

Solution. The time constant is defined as the time taken to reach an equilibrium temperature if the initial rate of temperature rise is maintained. The rate of heat dissipation is $q' \times$ Volume, so that the initial rate of temperature rise is $d\theta/dt = q'V/mc_p$, where V is the volume, m is the mass, and c_p is the specific heat. As soon as there is a temperature rise θ, the cooling rate is $hA\theta$, where h is the convection coefficient and A is the area. The rate of temperature rise is then $d\theta/dt = (q'V - hA\theta)/mc_p$. This equation may be re-arranged and integrated to give

$$\frac{t}{mc_p} = -\frac{1}{hA}\ln\left(1 - \frac{hA}{q'V}\theta\right)$$

and since $q'V/hA = \theta_{max}$, the equilibrium rise, this will give

$$\theta = \theta_{max}(1 - e^{-t/T})$$

where $T = mc_p/hA$, the time constant.

Hence the temperature rise θ after any time t may be calculated. For the particular problem, θ_{max} is $250/40 \times 0.12 = 52°C$, and the time constant is $20 \times 350/40 \times 0.12 = 1460$ sec, or 24.3 min.

5.2. The Solution of Transient Conduction Problems

The discussion is limited to one-dimensional transient conduction, in rectangular coordinates for which the equation is

$$\partial t/\partial t = \alpha(\partial^2 t/\partial x^2) \tag{(2.8)}$$

For the general problem numerical and graphical methods will be described.

It is necessary to replace equation (2.8) by a finite difference relationship. Figure 5.1 shows a plane slab uniformly divided into layers of thickness a, with a temperature contour at some time t_0.

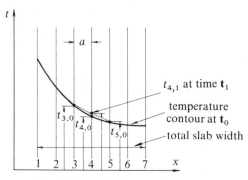

Fig. 5.1. The Schmidt construction.

Recalling the argument of section 4.1 it will be seen that the temperatures $t_{3,0}$, $t_{4,0}$, and $t_{5,0}$ are related:

$$t_{3,0} + t_{5,0} = 2t_{4,0} + \left(\frac{\partial^2 t}{\partial x^2}\right)_{4,0} a^2$$

and hence

$$\left(\frac{\partial^2 t}{\partial x^2}\right)_{4,0} = \frac{t_{3,0} + t_{5,0} - 2t_{4,0}}{a^2} \tag{5.1}$$

The finite difference relationship for $(\partial t/\partial t)$ is

$$\left(\frac{\partial t}{\partial t}\right)_{4,0} = \frac{t_{4,1} - t_{4,0}}{\Delta t} \tag{5.2}$$

where $t_{4,1}$ is the temperature at point 4 at time t_1, which is Δt after t_0. Equation (2.8) can now be replaced by

$$\frac{t_{4,1} - t_{4,0}}{\Delta t} = \alpha \left(\frac{t_{3,0} + t_{5,0} - 2t_{4,0}}{a^2}\right) \tag{5.3}$$

This may be arranged in two ways:

$$t_{4,1} = F\left[t_{3,0} + t_{5,0} + t_{4,0}\left(\frac{1}{F} - 2\right)\right] \tag{5.4}$$

and

$$t_{4,1} - t_{4,0} = 2F\left(\frac{t_{3,0} + t_{5,0}}{2} - t_{4,0}\right) \tag{5.5}$$

F is the Fourier number, $\Delta t \alpha / a^2$.

5.2.1. A Numerical Method. Equation 5.4 is suitable for performing a numerical solution. Values of Δt and a are chosen to give a suitable value of F. If $F = \frac{1}{2}$ then $t_{4,1}$ is simply the average of $t_{3,0}$ and $t_{5,0}$. For smaller values of F increased accuracy will be obtained. In order to solve a problem it is, of course, necessary to know the boundary temperatures after each time interval Δt.

Convection at a solid boundary can be allowed for in a numerical solution by setting up an energy equation for the boundary slab. The change in stored energy over the chosen time interval is equal to the conduction from the adjoining slab plus the convection from the boundary fluid. A relation between the fluid temperature and temperatures in the solid is thus obtained.

5.2.2. The Schmidt Graphical Method. This method was proposed by Binder[1] in 1910, and was later developed by Schmidt in 1924.[2] Figure 5.1 shows how the temperature $t_{4,1}$ is obtained graphically. If $F = \frac{1}{2}$ in equation (5.5), $t_{4,1}$ is seen to be the average of $t_{3,0}$ and $t_{5,0}$. When $t_{3,0}$ and $t_{5,0}$ are joined by a straight line, $t_{4,1}$ is the point where this line cuts line 4. Figure 5.2 shows the progress of a graphical procedure for finding the temperature history in a wall as the

Fig. 5.2. *The left face of the wall increases in temperature by θ for every time interval Δt.*

surface temperature rises linearly with time. Initially, the temperature contour is a horizontal line, t_0. The right-hand wall surface has remained at t_0 over the duration considered, but it must be appreciated that exact boundary conditions must be specified to enable a solution to be obtained.

The Schmidt method can be used when knowledge of surface temperatures is lacking. The more common situation is that the temperature history of an adjacent fluid is known, together with a suitable value of surface convection coefficient.

In Fig. 5.3, the temperature contours in both fluid and conducting solid at time 0 are shown. The heat transfer rate at the wall surface by convection must be equal to the conduction rate *at the wall*

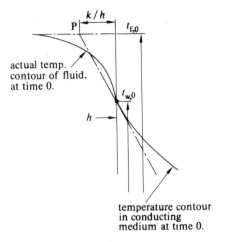

Fig. 5.3. *Convection at the surface.*

surface at time 0. The conduction rate is given by

$$q_x = -k\left(\frac{\partial t}{\partial x}\right)_{w, 0}$$

The convection rate is given by

$$q_x = -h(t_{w, 0} - t_{f, 0})$$

Hence

$$k\left(\frac{\partial t}{\partial x}\right)_{w, 0} = h(t_{w, 0} - t_{f, 0})$$

and

$$\left(\frac{\partial t}{\partial x}\right)_{w, 0} = \frac{t_{w, 0} - t_{f, 0}}{k/h}$$

If a triangle is constructed by drawing a tangent to the temperature gradient $(\partial t/\partial x)_{w, 0}$, with the tangent intersecting $t_{f, 0}$ produced horizontally at P, then the height of the triangle is clearly $(t_{w, 0} - t_{f, 0})$ and the base is k/h. So it is possible to imagine the real wall extended into the fluid region by an amount k/h, and the temperature history of the imaginary surface corresponds to the temperature history of the fluid. The possibility of the surface convection coefficient varying with time can also be accommodated in the graphical procedure for solving this type of problem. The construction involved is shown in Fig. 5.4.

In Fig. 5.4a, h is taken as being constant and therefore a vertical line may be drawn at a distance k/h from the left-hand surface of the plane specimen. Mesh lines are drawn as shown, at $\frac{1}{2}a$ either side of the surface, then continuing at intervals of a. The fluid temperatures $t_{f,0}$, $t_{f,1}$, etc., are then indicated on line 00. It is necessary that the temperature contour on the left of the surface is tangential to the temperature gradient at the surface, and this is achieved by drawing $t_{f,0}$, $t_{w,0}$, and $t_{1,0}$ as a straight line. The point representing

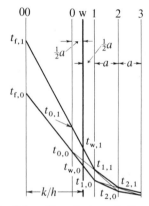

Fig. 5.4a.   Transient conduction at the wall surface, h constant.

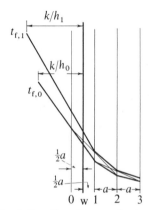

Fig. 5.4b.   Transient conduction at the wall surface, h variable.

temperature $t_{0,0}$ is clearly useful for constructional purposes, though the temperature itself has no meaning. In Fig. 5.4b the construction for a variable h is shown; it will be seen that $t_{f,1}$ has moved horizontally as well as vertically relative to $t_{f,0}$.

Having obtained the temperature time history for a particular problem it is possible, by simple repetitive calculations, to determine the quantities of energy entering, leaving, or being stored. The time interval between each temperature contour is Δt. Hence, the heat transfer by convection to the surface over the first time interval is

$$h\left(\frac{t_{f,1} + t_{f,0}}{2} - \frac{t_{w,1} + t_{w,0}}{2}\right)\Delta t \text{ heat units/unit area} \qquad (5.6)$$

i.e., h(average fluid − average wall temperature) × time interval. The summation of such calculations over all the time intervals will give the total heat transfer to the specimen. Energy being stored may be calculated in a similar manner by considering average slab temperatures before and after a given interval. Thus, the energy stored between 0 and 1 in the time scale for the initial half slab and second slab is

$$a\rho c_p\left[\left(\frac{t_{w,1}+t_{1,1}}{4}-\frac{t_{w,0}+t_{1,0}}{4}\right)+\left(\frac{t_{1,1}+t_{2,1}}{2}-\frac{t_{1,0}+t_{2,0}}{2}\right)\right]$$

$$\text{heat units/unit area} \qquad (5.7)$$

Alternatively, the total energy stored at time 1 relative to some datum temperature may be readily calculated.

Finally, two particular boundary conditions will be discussed.
Insulated surface. Since there can be no heat transfer at an insulated surface, the temperature gradient is therefore zero. Construction must proceed from the other surface, with the temperature profile horizontal over the insulated slab, as in Fig. 5.5.

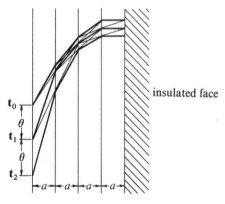

Fig. 5.5.   Effect of an insulated surface.

Surface temperature changes suddenly. When a body is suddenly immersed in a fluid of different temperature, a discontinuity of temperature exists at zero time. This initial temperature contour is shown in Fig. 5.6. It may be represented by the straight line drawn across the conducting film in the fluid. This, then, gives the first

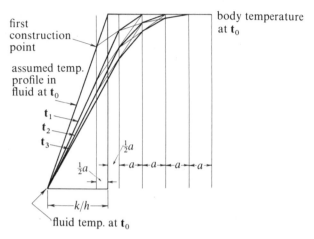

Fig. 5.6.   Sudden fluid temperature change at a surface.

construction point, from which the solution may proceed. It should be mentioned that the method just described is only approximate, since at zero time the surface temperature may have any value between its original temperature and the fluid temperature. A more rigorous procedure is described by Hsu.[3]

5.3. Periodic Temperature Changes at a Surface

A periodically changing surface temperature can also be dealt with by numerical or graphical methods, but the work involved is probably not justified in view of the fact that an analytical solution is not too lengthy for this particular boundary condition.

The problem to be considered is one in which a plane slab of material, referred to as a 'semi-infinite solid', is regarded as being infinitely thick, the periodic surface temperature existing at the face of the slab where $x = 0$. The surface temperature varies in a sinusoidal manner and, because of the assumption of infinite thickness, the temperature history within the material is controlled only by the surface variation. Further, conduction takes place in only one dimension, so that edge effects are neglected or the specimen is regarded as being sufficiently large in the y-direction for conduction to be one-dimensional over the area of material of interest. An additional assumption is that conditions are steady, which means that the cyclic variation of temperature at the surface has been going on for a time sufficiently long for temperatures elsewhere in the slab to be repeated identically in each cycle. The general result obtained, as will be seen, is that the interior temperature cycle lags behind the surface variation, depending on the depth and, in addition, has a diminished amplitude compared with the maximum surface values. This type of analysis finds application wherever a cyclic variation of temperature occurs, as in annual or daily temperature variation of buildings or the ground exposed to solar radiation, and, in the other extreme, in the cylinders of reciprocating engines. The chief restriction on the validity of the analysis is whether the object in question may be regarded as infinitely thick. The depth in the material at which the temperature amplitude has become, say, only 1 per cent of the surface value is the criterion by which this is judged.

The surface of the slab has a mean temperature t. It varies in a sinusoidal manner between an upper temperature limit of $t + (\theta_m)_0$ and a lower limit of $t - (\theta_m)_0$. Thus, if θ is the temperature difference between the actual temperature at any instant and the mean then, at the surface where $x = 0$, θ varies between $\pm (\theta_m)_0$ where θ_m denotes the maximum difference. Further, at some depth x in the slab, θ varies between $\pm(\theta_m)_x$. The frequency of the temperature variation is n cycles per unit time, so $1/n$ is the period of the variation. The boundary conditions of the problem are set by the sinusoidal temperature variation at the surface, given by

$$\theta = (\theta_m)_0 \sin(2\pi nt) \tag{5.8}$$

which is the value of θ at $x = 0$, and $\mathbf{t} = t$. At $x = 0$ and $\mathbf{t} = 0$, $\theta = 0$. In equation (5.8) $2\pi n$ is the angular velocity of the sine wave in rads/unit time.

Since θ is the temperature variation about a mean value t, θ may be regarded as the temperature variable since t is constant. For this case the one-dimensional unsteady equation, (2.8), becomes

$$\frac{\partial \theta}{\partial \mathbf{t}} = \alpha \left(\frac{\partial^2 \theta}{\partial x^2} \right) \tag{5.9}$$

Since θ varies sinusoidally at the surface, it can also be expected to do so within the solid, but between reducing limits and, consequently, the general form of solution of this differential equation which may be chosen as being applicable is

$$\theta = Ce^{-px} \sin(2\pi nt - qx) \tag{5.10}$$

where C, p, and q are constants to be determined. The constants p and q may be found by substituting equation (5.10) in equation (5.9). The partial differential coefficients found from (5.10) are

$$\frac{\partial \theta}{\partial t} = 2\pi n C e^{-px} \cos(2\pi nt - qx)$$

$$\frac{\partial \theta}{\partial x} = -pCe^{-px} \sin(2\pi nt - qx) - qCe^{-px} \cos(2\pi nt - qx)$$

$$\frac{\partial^2 \theta}{\partial x^2} = p^2 Ce^{-px} \sin(2\pi nt - qx) + pqCe^{-px} \cos(2\pi nt - qx)$$

$$+ pqCe^{-px} \cos(2\pi nt - qx) - q^2 Ce^{-px} \sin(2\pi nt - qx)$$

Hence, equation (5.9) becomes, noting that Ce^{-px} may be cancelled from all terms:

$$2\pi n \cos(2\pi nt - qx) = \alpha[p^2 \sin(2\pi nt - qx)$$

$$+ 2pq \cos(2\pi nt - qx) - q^2 \sin(2\pi nt - qx)]$$

$$\therefore \quad (2\pi n - 2pq\alpha) \cos(2\pi nt - qx) = \alpha(p^2 - q^2) \sin(2\pi nt - qx)$$

At $x = 0$ and $t = 0$, this reduces to

$$(2\pi n - 2pq\alpha) = 0$$

$$\therefore \quad pq = \pi n/\alpha$$

Further, as there is no sine term on the left, it follows that

$$p^2 - q^2 = 0$$

$$\text{or} \quad p = q$$

Thus, from these results,

$$p = q = \pm (\pi n/\alpha)^{0.5}$$

The negative solution of this has no meaning, and hence equation (5.10) now becomes:

$$\theta = C \exp[-x(\pi n/\alpha)^{0.5}] \sin[2\pi nt - x(\pi n/\alpha)^{0.5}] \quad (5.11)$$

This result may now be compared with the boundary condition at $x = 0$ and $t = t$. Thus (5.11) gives

$$\theta = C \sin 2\pi nt$$

and the boundary condition gives

$$\theta = (\theta_m)_0 \sin 2\pi nt$$

Thus comparing these two equations shows that $C = (\theta_m)_0$. The final solution is therefore

$$\theta = (\theta_m)_0 \exp[-x(\pi n/\alpha)^{0.5}] \sin[2\pi nt - x(\pi n/\alpha)^{0.5}] \qquad (5.12)$$

This equation shows that the maximum variation of θ decreases exponentially with x, the distance into the solid, according to the equation

$$(\theta_m)_x = (\theta_m)_0 \exp[-x(\pi n/\alpha)^{0.5}] \qquad (5.13)$$

The general form of the result given by equation (5.12) is shown in Figs. 5.7 and 5.8. In Fig. 5.7 the temperature variation with distance

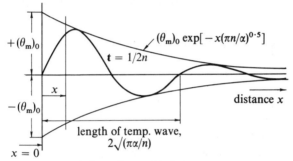

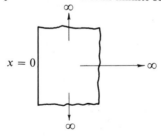

representation of a semi-infinite solid

Fig. 5.7. Established temperature variation vs. distance into solid, at $t = 1/2n$.

at a chosen time is shown, and in Fig. 5.8 temperature variations with time at the surface and depth x are shown. It will be seen that a temperature wave propagates into the solid, and also that the cyclic variation of temperature at some depth x lags behind the surface variation. The phase difference in temperature variation

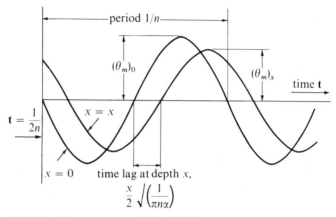

Fig. 5.8. Temperature variation with time at x = 0, and at depth x.

at depth x is given by $x(\pi n/\alpha)^{0.5}$. Hence the time lag of a certain temperature excess (diminished in value at depth x) will be given by

$$2\pi n \Delta t = x(\pi n/\alpha)^{0.5}$$

$$\therefore \quad \Delta t = \frac{x}{2}\left(\frac{1}{\pi n \alpha}\right)^{0.5} \quad (5.14)$$

Δt for a complete temperature wave of length X is $1/n$ hence, for a complete wave, the wave-length is given by

$$2\pi = X(\pi n/\alpha)^{0.5}$$

$$\therefore \quad X = 2(\pi \alpha/n)^{0.5} \quad (5.15)$$

Also, the velocity of propagation of the temperature wave into the solid is

$$U = \frac{X}{1/n} = 2(\pi n \alpha)^{0.5} \quad (5.16)$$

The ratio of maximum temperature variations about the mean may be compared using equation (5.13). Thus:

$$\frac{(\theta_m)_x}{(\theta_m)_0} = \exp[-x(\pi n/\alpha)^{0.5}]$$

If it is required to determine the distance x at which $(\theta_m)_x$ has decreased to a certain percentage of $(\theta_m)_0$, this result may be re-arranged to give

$$x = \frac{\ln(\theta_m)_0/(\theta_m)_x}{(\pi n/\alpha)^{0.5}} \quad (5.17)$$

EXAMPLE 5.2

Calculate the depth below which a water main must be placed to prevent it freezing if it is assumed that the surface temperature varies sinusoidally between 20 and 100°F in a period of 365 days. Take $\alpha = 0.016 \, \text{ft}^2/\text{h}$.

Solution. $(\theta_m)_0 = 40°F$, and the mean surface temperature is 60°F. Hence $(\theta_m)_x = 60 - 32 = 28°F$.

$n = 1/24 \times 365$

Using equation (5.17),

$$x = \frac{\ln 40/28}{(\pi/24 \times 365 \times 0.016)^{\frac{1}{2}}} = 2.4 \, \text{ft}.$$

Thus, the water main should be placed below this depth to prevent freezing.

Finally, the heat transfer rate at the wall surface, at $x = 0$, may be determined from

$$q = \frac{Q}{A} = -k\left(\frac{\partial \theta}{\partial x}\right)_{x=0}$$

and from equation (5.12),

$$\left(\frac{\partial \theta}{\partial x}\right)_{x=0} = -(\theta_m)_0(\pi n/\alpha)^{0.5}(\sin 2\pi nt + \cos 2\pi nt)$$

Using the identity,

$$\sin(2\pi nt + \pi/4) = \sin 2\pi nt \cos \pi/4 + \sin \pi/4 \cos 2\pi nt$$

$$= (1/\sqrt{2})(\sin 2\pi nt + \cos 2\pi nt)$$

it follows that

$$\left(\frac{\partial \theta}{\partial x}\right)_{x=0} = -(\theta_m)_0(2\pi n/\alpha)^{0.5} \sin(2\pi nt + \pi/4)$$

and hence,

$$q = k(\theta_m)_0(2\pi n/\alpha)^{0.5} \sin(2\pi nt + \pi/4) \qquad (5.18)$$

From equation (5.18) it will be seen that the surface heat transfer rate varies sinusoidally and with the same frequency as the surface temperature, but leading by a period of $1/8n$. The total heat transfer at the wall is given by

$$\int q \, dt = \int k(\theta_m)_0 (2\pi n/\alpha)^{0.5} \sin(2\pi nt + \pi/4) \, dt$$

$$= -k(\theta_m)_0 (1/2\pi n\alpha)^{0.5} \cos(2\pi nt + \pi/4) \text{ heat/unit area} \qquad (5.19)$$

Thus the energy stored, as represented by an integral of heat transfer rate at the surface, also varies with the same frequency, but it will be found that it lags behind the surface temperature variation by a period of $1/8n$. Further, it will be apparent that the surface heat transfer is both to and from the solid and that the energy stored is in sequence both positive and negative relative to the mean temperature.

PROBLEMS

1. Steel strip of thickness 1·27 cm emerges from a rolling mill at a temperature of 538°C and with a velocity of 2·44 m/sec. The strip is cooled in such a way that its surface temperature falls linearly with distance from the mill at a rate of 110°C/m.

Derive a finite difference method for dealing with this case of transient heat conduction assuming that heat flows only in the direction normal to the strip faces.

Subdividing the strip into six increments of thickness, determine the temperature distribution in the strip and the heat flux from the surface at a position 2·74 m from the mill. (For steel take thermal conductivity 43·3 J/m s deg C, thermal diffusivity 0.98×10^{-5} m²/s.) (Ans. 3.41×10^6 J/m² s.) (*University of Manchester*).

2. A steel pipe, 2·54 cm wall thickness, is initially at a uniform temperature of 16°C when a liquid metal at 572°C is pumped through it for a time of 10 sec and with a surface coefficient of 2840 J/m² s deg C. It may be assumed that the pipe diameter is large enough for the wall to be considered plane, that no heat loss occurs from the outside of the pipe and from the inside after the flow of liquid metal has ceased.

Derive a numerical method to deal with this case using finite increments of thickness and making the simplification that the heat capacity of the surface half-increment is negligible. Using four increments determine the wall temperature distribution after 18 sec. (For steel take thermal conductivity 40·7 J/m s deg C, density 7530 kg/m³ and specific heat 536 J/kg deg C.) (Ans. 280°C, 174°C.) (*University of Manchester*).

3. Thermo-couples in a plane wall, made of concrete 15 in. thick, which is receiving heat on one side, are used to measure the temperature distribution across the wall. At a particular instant, the following equation is found to

represent approximately the temperature $T°$F.

$$T = 75 - 6y - 20y^2$$

where y ft is measured normally to the surface of the wall.
   For an effective area of 20 ft^2, estimate the following:
   (i) the rate at which heat enters the wall
   (ii) the rate at which heat is stored in the wall
   (iii) the rate of change of temperature at the mid-plane of the wall.
   Assume that the concrete has a density of 140 lb/ft^3, a specific heat capacity of 0·20 Btu/lb deg F and a thermal conductivity of 0·45 Btu/h ft deg F, and that these properties are constant and uniform. (Ans. 54 Btu/h at $y = 0$, -450 Btu/h, $-0·642$ deg F/h.) (*Queen Mary College, London*).

4. Given the differential equation $(\partial t/\partial \tau) = \alpha(\partial^2 t/\partial x^2)$, for unsteady conduction in a 'one-dimensional' wall, show that the temperature $t_{n,\,p+1}$ at some section n and time instant $(p + 1)$ can be calculated approximately from

$$t_{n,\,p+1} = F\left[t_{n+1,\,p} + t_{n-1,\,p} + \left(\frac{1}{F} - 2\right)t_{n,\,p}\right]$$

The temperatures in the right-hand bracket are values at equidistant sections $(n - 1), n, (n + 1)$, preceding $(p + 1)$ by a finite time interval $\Delta\tau$; $F = \alpha\Delta\tau/\Delta x^2$ is the Fourier number.
   Plane 1 is a distance $\Delta x/2$ to the right of a wall surface. Prove that, if the convection coefficient and temperature of the fluid to the left of the surface is h and t_s respectively,

$$t_{1,\,p+1} = F\left[t_{2,\,p} + \frac{2B}{2+B}t_{s,\,p} + \left(\frac{1}{F} - \frac{2+3B}{2+B}\right)t_{1,\,p}\right]$$

where $B = h\Delta x/k$.
   In a particular problem, $k = 0·5$ Btu/ft h deg F, $\alpha = 0·021$ ft^2/h, $\Delta x = 2$ in., $h = 2$ Btu/ft^{2}h deg F. At time $\tau = 0$ all temperatures are 40°F and t_s rises linearly with time at the rate of 7·5°F/h. Take $F = \frac{1}{4}$, and calculate temperatures within the wall after 1 hour. (Ans. plane 1, 40·87°F; plane 2, 40·075°F.) (*University of Bristol*).

5. A bare copper cable 1 in. diameter, is situated in still air at 60°F. A current is passed along the cable such that heat is released within the cable at the rate of 20 Btu/h ft length. Determine the equilibrium temperature of the surface of the cable if the heat transfer coefficient for natural convection from the surface of the cable is 0·45 $\theta^{\frac{1}{4}}$ Btu/ft^2 h deg F where θ is the temperature difference (°F) between the surface and the ambient air. Neglect radiation.
   If the current is now stopped, estimate the time for the copper to cool to a temperature of 65°F. It may be assumed that at any instant the temperature is uniform across the copper. For copper, the density ρ is 560 lb/ft^3; and the specific heat c is 0·09 Btu/lb deg F. (Ans. 120·8°F, 2·87 h.) (*University of Glasgow*).

6. In order to carry out an approximate analysis of a butt-welding process, it is assumed that there is a uniform rate of heat generation at the contact face between the two bars, that heat conduction occurs only in a direction normal to the contact face and that the physical properties of the bars are constant. Derive a numerical method to deal with this case by sub-dividing the bars into finite increments of length.

Apply the method to obtain the approximate temperature distribution in two similar steel bars, initially at 16°C, after 10 sec. The heat generation rate is 1005 J/cm² sec and this acts for a period of 5 sec. Use 0·635 cm increments of length and, for steel, take thermal conductivity = 45 J/m s deg C, density = 7690 kg/m³ and specific heat = 545 J/kg deg C. (Ans. 1195°C maximum at joint, after 10 sec: 384°C.) (*University of Manchester*).

7. A steel slab 2·54 cm thick is initially at a uniform temperature of 650°C. It is cooled by quenching in water which may be assumed to reduce the surface temperature suddenly to 93·5°C. Derive a numerical method to deal with this case by considering a finite number of interior slices. The heat flow may be assumed normal to the sides of the slab. Use the method to determine the time required to reduce the centre temperature to 450°C (sub-divide the slab into eight slices). For steel take a thermal diffusivity = 1·16 × 10⁻⁵ m²/s. (Ans. 3·47 sec.) (*University of Manchester*).

8. A large steel plate 7·62 cm thick initially uniformly at 816°C is quenched in oil at 38°C. If the oil temperature remains constant and there is negligible surface resistance, estimate the time required to reduce to 427°C:
   (*a*) the average temperature of the slab,
   (*b*) the centre-line temperature.
Thermal diffusivity of steel = 1·032 × 10⁻⁵ m²/s. (Ans. 22·3 sec, 52·0 sec.) (*University of Leeds*).

9. A large piece of steel plate 1 ft thick is placed on a trolley and pushed into a heat treating furnace operating at 560°F. If the plate is initially at 60°F throughout, calculate how long it will take to heat the bottom face to 500°F. Assume that the plate receives heat only through the upper face, the side effects being negligible and the lower face insulated.

The combined effects of convection and radiation from the furnace may be accounted for by a single heat transfer coefficient = 10 Btu/ft² h deg F.
The steel has the following properties:
                Thermal conductivity 25 Btu/ft h deg F.
                Thermal diffusivity   0·5 ft²/h.
(Ans. 12 h.) (*University of Leeds*).

10. An internal combustion engine runs at 2500 r.p.m. The thermal diffusivity of the carbon steel of the cylinder walls is 1·16 × 10⁻⁵ m²/s. The temperature of the cylinder wall varies sinusoidally between 500 and 100°C. Assuming that the cylinder wall behaves like a semi-infinite solid, determine the depth into the wall in cm at which the temperature amplitude has decreased to 1 per

cent of the surface value, and plot the heat transfer rate at the wall surface over a complete cycle. $k = 40$ J/m s deg C. (Ans. 0·194 cm, limits $\pm 2·68 \times 10^4$ kW/m^2.)

REFERENCES

1. Binder, L. *Dissertation*, München (1910).
2. Schmidt, E. *Festschrift zum siebzigsten Geburtstag August Föppl*, Springer, Berlin (1924).
3. Hsu, S. T. *Engineering Heat Transfer*, D. Van Nostrand Company, Inc., New York, 103, (1963).

Section 2
Heat Transfer by Convection

Before proceeding to the treatment of this subject, it is necessary to explain the approach adopted. The reader will be aware that the purpose is to describe the methods by which the convection coefficient may be predicted. The subject of convection heat transfer may be conveniently divided according to the nature of the fluid flow. Without motion of the fluid there would be no convection, and a knowledge of the behaviour of fluids near solid boundaries is a necessary prerequisite to the study of this form of energy transfer. An analytical approach involves a knowledge of the temperature gradient in the fluid at the solid surface, and this entails the use of the basic equations governing the motion of the fluid. This approach is only practicable in simple cases of laminar flow and is introduced in chapter 6.

Reynolds analogy between heat transfer and fluid friction, and dimensional analysis, have more general application to the study of convection and these topics are introduced in chapter 7.

Chapter 8 deals with natural convection, in which only buoyancy forces in the fluid are responsible for the fluid motion, using dimensional analysis.

Chapters 9 and 10 deal with separated flow convection and convection with phase change, largely from a descriptive point of view. Separated flow, in which the boundary layer leaves the solid surface, occurs in cross flow in tube banks, and the convection processes involved are important in a variety of heat exchange devices. Convection with phase change includes boiling and condensing heat transfer, both of which are of great importance in steam power plant.

The final chapter in the section gives a basic introduction to the study of mass transfer. It has already been observed that convection heat transfer takes place when there is motion of the fluid material relative to the solid surface. It was assumed that the fluid was a single substance, as far as the overall effects were concerned. This will not always be the case, and many situations exist in which convection or diffusion of a component within a mixture occurs, or in which a component of the mixture evaporates or condenses at a surface. Processes of this type, which involve a transfer of material within the fluid as a whole, and which are generally accompanied by an energy transfer, form the subject matter of Mass Transfer. Mass transfer theory is of importance in the design of a diversity of plant, including water cooling towers, drying equipment, and air conditioners.

6

Forced convection: consideration of the thermal boundary layer

This chapter shows how the convection coefficient h may be determined analytically for simple cases of laminar flow. Some familiarity with the behaviour of viscous fluids flowing over solid surfaces is assumed. The important aspects of laminar boundary layers are illustrated in Figs. 6.1 to 6.4; some comparisons with turbulent boundary layers are also shown. Thus Fig. 6.1 shows the general shape of the velocity distribution in laminar and turbulent boundary layers on a flat plate. In the turbulent case, the existence of a laminar

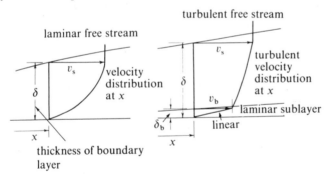

Fig. 6.1. *Velocity distributions in laminar and turbulent boundary layers.*

sub-layer with linear velocity distribution is assumed. Figure 6.2 shows boundary layer growth at the entrance of a tube, together with fully developed profiles for laminar and turbulent flow. In the case of laminar flow, there is a simple relationship between the starting length, diameter, and diameter Reynolds number:[1]

$$\frac{L_s}{d} = 0.05 Re_d \qquad (6.1)$$

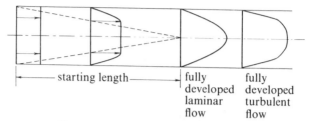

|——————— starting length ———————| fully developed laminar flow   fully developed turbulent flow

Fig. 6.2.   Boundary layer growth in a tube.

The velocity profiles follow closely the following equations:

for laminar flow:
$$\frac{v}{v_a} = \frac{y}{r}\left(2 - \frac{y}{r}\right)$$
(6.2)

for turbulent flow:
$$\frac{v}{v_a} = \left(\frac{y}{r}\right)^{\frac{1}{7}}$$
(6.3)

where v is the velocity y from the tube wall, v_a is the velocity at the axis. Velocity profiles on a flat plate also follow closely parabolic and $\frac{1}{7}$th power law relationships, in laminar and turbulent flow.

The shear stress in the laminar boundary layer (see Fig. 6.3), is related to the velocity gradient by the equation

$$\tau = \mu\frac{dv}{dy}$$
(6.4)

where μ is the coefficient of molecular viscosity. It has units of N s/m² or the equivalent.

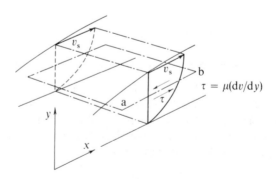

Fig. 6.3.   Shear stress.

Thermal boundary layers also exist. These are flow regions where the fluid temperature changes from the free stream value to the value at the surface or wall. Examples in flow over a flat plate are shown in Fig. 6.4.

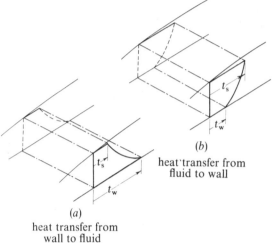

(b)
heat transfer from
fluid to wall

(a)
heat transfer from
wall to fluid

Fig. 6.4.   Examples of temperature boundary layers.

6.1. Equations of the Laminar Boundary Layer

There are two methods by which forced convection may be studied by consideration of the boundary layer. The first is to use the differential equations of motion and energy in the boundary layer to deduce the temperature gradient in the fluid at the wall, and hence the convection coefficient, and the second is to use the integral equations of motion and energy. In the second method the same laws of viscous flow, mass continuity, and energy conservation are applied to a control volume within the boundary layer, rather than to an infinitesimal element of fluid as in the derivation of the differential equations.

6.1.1. The Differential Equations of Motion and Energy in a Laminar Boundary Layer.
The equations of motion of a viscous fluid in three dimensions are known as the Navier–Stokes equations. They are derived by considering the acceleration of a fluid element produced by the resultant of the forces acting on the element. These

forces consist of static pressure forces (from applied pressure gradients), body forces (such as buoyancy forces), normal and shear stresses. The derivation may be found in the more advanced texts of heat transfer, e.g., ref. 2. When these equations are applied to forced flow in a laminar boundary layer with a negligible pressure gradient, they reduce to a single equation:

$$v_x \frac{\partial v_x}{\partial x} + v_y \frac{\partial v_x}{\partial y} = v \frac{\partial^2 v_x}{\partial y^2} \tag{6.5}$$

where $v = \mu/\rho$, the kinematic viscosity.

It should be pointed out that though v_y is small, $\partial v_x/\partial y$ is large and hence $v_y \partial v_x/\partial y$ may not be neglected.

The energy equation of the fluid element in two-dimensional flow may be derived by considering net rates of convected and conducted energy into the element in the x- and y-coordinates, which must be zero in steady state conditions. A further term arises due to the degradation of mechanical energy into thermal energy due to viscous action of the fluid. This term is small, however, and may be conveniently neglected. Further, mass continuity must apply and the final result is:

$$\alpha \left(\frac{\partial^2 t}{\partial x^2} + \frac{\partial^2 t}{\partial y^2} \right) - \left(v_x \frac{\partial t}{\partial x} + v_y \frac{\partial t}{\partial y} \right) = 0 \tag{6.6}$$

If temperature in this equation is replaced by a temperature difference, $\theta = (t - t_w)$, and if $\partial^2 t/\partial x^2$ is neglected as being very small compared with other terms, then equation (6.6) becomes, assuming t_w to be a constant,

$$v_x \frac{\partial \theta}{\partial x} + v_y \frac{\partial \theta}{\partial y} = \alpha \frac{\partial^2 \theta}{\partial y^2} \tag{6.7}$$

Consideration of equations (6.5) and (6.7) shows that they are strikingly similar. It will be seen that the two equations are identical in form if $\alpha = v$. If this is so the two equations must lead to identical non-dimensionalized temperature and velocity contours across the boundary layer. Inspection of α and v shows that they have identical units (length²/time), and consequently their ratio, v/α, is dimensionless. This group is known as the Prandtl number. For the special case of $\alpha = v$, the Prandtl number is 1. In terms of the basic properties,

$$Pr = \frac{v}{\alpha} = \frac{\mu}{\rho} \cdot \frac{\rho c_p}{k} = \frac{c_p \mu}{k} \tag{6.8}$$

In physical terms, the Prandtl number is the ratio of fluid properties controlling contours in the fluid and thermal boundary layers, and from equations (6.5) and (6.7) the contours are identical when the Prandtl number is 1.

6.1.2. The Integral Motion and Energy Equations of the Laminar Boundary Layer. To consider the motion in the boundary layer, an elemental control volume is chosen that extends from the wall to just beyond the limit of the boundary layer in the y-direction, is dx thick in the x-direction, and has unit depth in the z-direction. This is shown in Fig. 6.5. An equation is sought which relates the net rate of change of momentum in the x-direction to the net force acting in the x-direction.

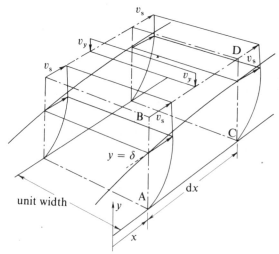

Fig. 6.5. *Elemental control volume in laminar boundary layer.*

The rate of change of momentum across the face AB will be

$$\int_0^\delta \rho v_x^2 \, dy$$

Similarly, the rate of change of momentum across the face CD will be

$$\int_0^\delta \rho v_x^2 \, dy + \frac{d}{dx} \int_0^\delta \rho v_x^2 \, dy \, dx$$

Fluid also enters the control volume across the face BD at the rate

$$\frac{d}{dx} \int_0^\delta \rho v_x \, dy \, dx$$

This is the difference between the fluid leaving across face CD and entering across face AB. The fluid entering across face BD has a velocity v_s in the x-direction, hence the rate of change of momentum in the x-direction is

$$v_s \frac{d}{dx} \int_0^\delta \rho v_x \, dy \, dx$$

Hence the net rate of change of momentum is

$$\frac{d}{dx} \int_0^\delta \rho v_x^2 \, dy \, dx - v_s \frac{d}{dx} \int_0^\delta \rho v_x \, dy \, dx$$

Pressure forces will act on faces AB and CD, and a shear force will act on face AC. There will be no shear force on face BD since this is at the limit of the boundary layer and $dv_x/dy = 0$. The net force acting on the control volume in the x-direction will be

$$p_x \delta - \left(p_x + \frac{dp_x}{dx} dx \right) \delta - \tau_w \, dx = - \delta \frac{dp_x}{dx} dx - \tau_w \, dx$$

The pressure gradient may be neglected as small compared with the shear force at the wall, and the equality of the net rate of change of momentum and the net force gives

$$\frac{d}{dx} \int_0^\delta \rho v_x (v_s - v_x) \, dy = \tau_w \tag{6.9}$$

This is the integral equation of motion in the laminar boundary layer, and was first derived by von Kármán.[3]

The integral energy equation may be derived in much the same way. In this case, a control volume extending beyond the limits of both temperature and velocity boundary layers may be considered initially, Fig. 6.6. The principle of conservation of energy applied to this control volume will involve the enthalpy and kinetic energy of fluid entering and leaving, and heat transfer by conduction at the wall. Kinetic energy may be neglected as being small in comparison

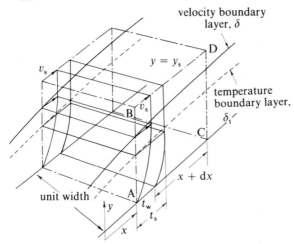

Fig. 6.6. *Control volume in temperature and velocity boundary layers.*

with other quantities. The enthalpy of the fluid flowing across face AB is

$$\int_0^{y_s} c_p \rho v_x t \, dy$$

and across face CD

$$\int_0^{y_s} c_p \rho v_x t \, dy + \frac{d}{dx} \int_0^{y_s} c_p \rho v_x t \, dy \, dx$$

Fluid will also enter the control volume across face BD at the rate

$$\frac{d}{dx} \int_0^{y_s} \rho v_x \, dy \, dx$$

Again this is the difference between the flow rate out at face CD and in at face AB. The enthalpy of this fluid will be

$$c_p t_s \frac{d}{dx} \int_0^{y_s} \rho v_x \, dy \, dx$$

Finally, heat transfer by conduction across the wall at AC will amount to

$$-k \, dx \left(\frac{\partial t}{\partial y} \right)_{y=0}$$

For conservation of energy:

$$c_p t_s \frac{d}{dx} \int_0^{y_s} \rho v_x \, dy \, dx - \frac{d}{dx} \int_0^{y_s} \rho c_p t v_x \, dy \, dx - k \, dx \left(\frac{\partial t}{\partial y}\right)_{y=0} = 0 \quad (6.10)$$

Beyond the limit of the temperature boundary layer, the temperature is constant at t_s, and hence the integration need only be taken up to $y = \delta_t$. Equation (6.10) therefore gives

$$\frac{d}{dx} \int_0^{\delta_t} (t_s - t) v_x \, dy - \alpha \left(\frac{\partial t}{\partial y}\right)_{y=0} = 0 \quad (6.11)$$

This, then, is the integral energy equation of the laminar boundary layer.

6.2. Laminar Forced Convection on a Flat Plate

The integral equations (6.9) and (6.11) will now be applied to the problem of laminar forced convection on a flat plate. The method is due to Eckert.[4] The first step is to use the integral equation of motion to derive an equation for boundary layer thickness. The velocity contour may be assumed to be of the form

$$v_x = a + by + cy^2 + dy^3$$

where a, b, c, and d are constants. The constants may be found by applying known boundary conditions. Thus $v_x = 0$ at $y = 0$, and hence $a = 0$. Also $v_x = v_s$ at $y = \delta$, and $(\partial v_x/\partial y)_\delta = 0$ at $y = \delta$. Further, since both v_x and v_y are zero at $y = 0$, it follows from (6.5) that $\partial^2 v_x/\partial y^2 = 0$, at $y = 0$. These results lead to

$$b = \frac{3}{2} \frac{v_s}{\delta}, \quad c = 0, \quad d = -\frac{v_s}{2\delta^3}$$

and hence

$$\frac{v_x}{v_s} = \frac{3}{2}\left(\frac{y}{\delta}\right) - \frac{1}{2}\left(\frac{y}{\delta}\right)^3 \quad (6.12)$$

Applying the integral equation of motion,

$$\frac{d}{dx} \int_0^\delta \rho v_x (v_s - v_x) \, dy = \tau_w$$

$$= \frac{d}{dx} \int_0^\delta \rho v_s^2 \left[\frac{3}{2}\left(\frac{y}{\delta}\right) - \frac{1}{2}\left(\frac{y}{\delta}\right)^3\right] \cdot \left[1 - \frac{3}{2}\left(\frac{y}{\delta}\right) + \frac{1}{2}\left(\frac{y}{\delta}\right)^3\right] dy$$

$$= \mu \left(\frac{dv_x}{dy}\right)_{y=0}$$

The wall shear stress is found by considering the velocity gradient at $y = 0$; this is found to be $3v_s/2\delta$. The above equation leads to

$$\frac{d}{dx}\rho v_s^2 \frac{39\delta}{280} = \frac{3}{2}\mu \frac{v_s}{\delta}$$

$$\therefore \qquad \rho v_s^2 \, d\delta = \frac{3}{2} \cdot \frac{280}{39} \frac{\mu v_s}{\delta} dx$$

$$\therefore \qquad \delta \, d\delta = \frac{140}{13} \cdot \frac{v}{v_s} dx$$

On integration

$$\frac{\delta^2}{2} = \frac{140vx}{13v_s} + C$$

$C = 0$, since $\delta = 0$ at $x = 0$

$$\therefore \qquad \delta^2 = \frac{280vx}{13v_s}$$

or

$$\frac{\delta}{x} = \frac{4 \cdot 64}{Re_x^{\frac{1}{2}}} \qquad (6.13)$$

This result, due to Pohlhausen,[5] is required later on in considering the integral energy equation.

The temperature distribution in the boundary layer is assumed to follow a similar law to the velocity distribution. Thus:

$$\theta = (t - t_w) = ay + by^2 + cy^3$$

where, again, a, b, and c are constants. The boundary conditions are that at $y = \delta_t$ (the thickness of the temperature boundary layer), $\theta = \theta_s$ and also $(\partial\theta/\partial y)_{\delta_t} = 0$. Also, from equation (6.7) it follows that $(\partial^2\theta/\partial y^2)_{y=0} = 0$ because v_x and v_y are both zero at $y = 0$. From these conditions it follows that

$$a = \frac{3}{2}\frac{\theta_s}{\delta_t}, \quad b = 0, \quad c = -\frac{\theta_s}{2\delta_t^3}$$

and hence

$$\frac{\theta}{\theta_s} = \frac{3}{2}\left(\frac{y}{\delta_t}\right) - \frac{1}{2}\left(\frac{y}{\delta_t}\right)^3 \qquad (6.14)$$

Turning to the integral energy equation, the substitutions
$\theta = (t - t_w)$ and $\theta_s = (t_s - t_w)$ are made to give

$$\frac{\mathrm{d}}{\mathrm{d}x}\int_0^{\delta_t} (\theta_s - \theta)v_x\,\mathrm{d}y - \alpha\left(\frac{\partial\theta}{\partial y}\right)_{y=0} = 0 \tag{6.15}$$

From the temperature equation (6.14) it follows that

$$\alpha\left(\frac{\partial\theta}{\partial y}\right)_{y=0} = \alpha\frac{3\theta_s}{2\delta_t}$$

This result is substituted in equation (6.15) together with the expressions for θ and v_x to give:

$$\frac{\mathrm{d}}{\mathrm{d}x}\int_0^{\delta_t}\left[\theta_s - \frac{3}{2}\left(\frac{y}{\delta_t}\right)\theta_s + \frac{1}{2}\left(\frac{y}{\delta_t}\right)^3\theta_s\right]\cdot\left[\frac{3}{2}\left(\frac{y}{\delta}\right)v_s - \frac{1}{2}\left(\frac{y}{\delta}\right)^3 v_s\right]\mathrm{d}y = \alpha\frac{3\theta_s}{2\delta_t}$$

A useful substitution is that $\lambda = \delta_t/\delta$.

$$\therefore \quad \frac{\mathrm{d}}{\mathrm{d}x}\theta_s v_s\int_0^{\delta_t}\left[1 - \frac{3}{2}\left(\frac{y}{\lambda\delta}\right) + \frac{1}{2}\left(\frac{y}{\lambda\delta}\right)^3\right]\cdot\left[\frac{3}{2}\left(\frac{y}{\delta}\right) - \frac{1}{2}\left(\frac{y}{\delta}\right)^3\right]\mathrm{d}y$$

$$= \alpha\frac{3\theta_s}{2\lambda\delta}$$

This then leads to

$$\frac{\mathrm{d}}{\mathrm{d}x}\left[\theta_s v_s\delta_t\left(\frac{3\lambda}{20} - \frac{3\lambda^3}{280}\right)\right] = \alpha\frac{3\theta_s}{2\lambda\delta}$$

It is convenient here to neglect the term $3\lambda^3/280$ as being small in comparison with $3\lambda/20$. This is justified since λ has the value of 1 if $Pr = 1$, and will not be far removed from 1 at other values of Pr fairly close to 1. Hence

$$\frac{\mathrm{d}}{\mathrm{d}x}\frac{3\lambda\delta_t}{20} = \alpha\frac{3}{2\lambda\delta v_s}$$

$$\therefore \quad \frac{\mathrm{d}}{\mathrm{d}x}(\lambda^2\delta) = \frac{10\alpha}{v_s\lambda\delta}$$

$$\therefore \quad 2\lambda\delta\frac{\mathrm{d}\lambda}{\mathrm{d}x} + \lambda^2\frac{\mathrm{d}\delta}{\mathrm{d}x} = \frac{10\alpha}{v_s\lambda\delta}$$

$$\therefore \quad 2\lambda^2\delta^2\frac{\mathrm{d}\lambda}{\mathrm{d}x} + \lambda^3\delta\frac{\mathrm{d}\delta}{\mathrm{d}x} = \frac{10\alpha}{v_s}$$

Equation (6.13) for δ may now be substituted.

$$\frac{\delta}{x} = \frac{4\cdot64}{Re_x^{\frac{1}{2}}}, \quad \text{and hence} \quad \delta = 4\cdot64\left(\frac{xv}{v_s}\right)^{\frac{1}{2}}$$

$$\therefore \quad 2\lambda^2\frac{21\cdot6xv}{v_s}\cdot\frac{d\lambda}{dx} + \frac{\lambda^3}{2}\cdot\frac{21\cdot6v}{v_s} = \frac{10\alpha}{v_s}$$

$$\therefore \quad 4\lambda^2 x\frac{d\lambda}{dx} + \lambda^3 = \frac{0\cdot93\alpha}{v} \tag{6.16}$$

This equation may be solved by making the substitution $\lambda^3 = p$, and $p = x^n$, and the solution obtained is:

$$\left(\frac{\delta_t}{\delta}\right)^3 = \frac{0\cdot93}{Pr} + \frac{M}{x^{\frac{3}{4}}}$$

noting that $\alpha/v = Pr$, and M is a constant of integration. The thickness of the thermal boundary layer will be 0 at the beginning of the heated section, at $x = x_h$, say, and hence

$$M = -\frac{0\cdot93x_h^{\frac{3}{4}}}{Pr}$$

and finally:

$$\left(\frac{\delta_t}{\delta}\right)^3 = \frac{0\cdot93}{Pr}\left[1 - \left(\frac{x_h}{x}\right)^{\frac{3}{4}}\right]$$

This result may be simplified further by assuming that the plate is heated along its entire length, or $x_h = 0$, in Fig. 6.7,

$$\text{hence} \quad \frac{\delta_t}{\delta} = \left(\frac{0\cdot93}{Pr}\right)^{\frac{1}{3}}$$

$$\left. \begin{array}{c} \\ \\ \end{array} \right\} \tag{6.17}$$

$$\text{or, approximately,} \quad \frac{\delta_t}{\delta} = \frac{1}{Pr^{\frac{1}{3}}}$$

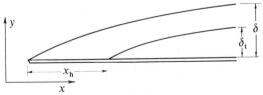

Fig. 6.7. *Laminar forced convection on a flat plate. Heating commences x_h from the leading edge.*

Using the equations for δ_t, δ, and the value of $(\partial\theta/\partial y)_{y=0}$ it is possible to determine the heat transfer at the wall, since

$$q_w = k\left(\frac{\partial\theta}{\partial y}\right)_{y=0} = k\frac{3\theta_s}{2\delta_t}, \quad \text{from (6.14)}$$

The heat transfer rate at the wall is expressed non-dimensionally. q_w/θ_s is the heat transfer coefficient h, and the group hx/k is the dimensionless Nusselt number, Nu. It is interpreted as the ratio of two lengths, the characteristic linear dimension of the system, and an equivalent conducting film of thickness δ'_t. Figure 6.8 shows

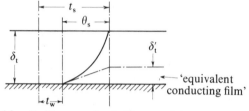

Fig. 6.8. *To illustrate the significance of the Nusselt number.*

how δ'_t is defined. The heat transfer at the wall is $q_w = h\theta_s$ and may be expressed as $q_w = (k/\delta'_t)\theta_s$. It follows that $h = k/\delta'_t$ and hence

$$Nu = \frac{hx}{k} = \frac{x}{\delta'_t}$$

The linear dimension of the system is generally large in comparison with δ'_t.

A Nusselt number may therefore be obtained:

$$Nu_x = \frac{q_w x}{\theta_s k} = \frac{3x}{2\delta_t} = \frac{3x\,Re_x^{\frac{1}{2}}\,Pr^{\frac{1}{3}}}{2(0\cdot93)^{\frac{1}{3}}4\cdot64x}$$

using (6.17) to eliminate δ_t, and (6.13) to eliminate δ.

$$\therefore \quad Nu_x = 0\cdot332 Re_x^{\frac{1}{2}}\,Pr^{\frac{1}{3}} \tag{6.18}$$

This gives the local Nusselt number at some distance x from the leading edge of the plate. The average value of the convection coefficient h, over the distance 0 to x is given by:

$$\bar{h} = \frac{1}{x}\int_0^x h\,dx$$

where

$$h = 0.332k\left(\frac{v_s}{vx}\right)^{\frac{1}{2}} Pr^{\frac{1}{3}}, \quad \text{from equation (6.18)}$$

$$\therefore \quad \bar{h} = \frac{k}{x} \frac{0.332}{\frac{1}{2}} \left(\frac{v_s x}{v}\right)^{\frac{1}{2}} Pr^{\frac{1}{3}}$$

$$= 0.664k\left(\frac{v_s}{vx}\right)^{\frac{1}{2}} Pr^{\frac{1}{3}}$$

and

$$\overline{Nu}_x = 0.664\, Re_x^{\frac{1}{2}}\, Pr^{\frac{1}{3}} \qquad (6.19)$$

This equation expresses in non-dimensional form the heat transfer by convection at the surface of a flat plate. Examples on the use of equations of this type will be found in the next chapter.

6.3. Laminar Forced Convection in a Tube

Laminar forced convection in a tube will be considered for the case of fully developed flow and constant heat flux at the wall. For fully developed flow it may be assumed that the velocity profile has a parabolic shape. It is first necessary to derive the energy equation for flow in a tube. To do this, a small cylindrical element of flow may be considered, as in Fig. 6.9. The element is of length dx, radius r on the inside, and radius r + dr on the outside. Energy will flow into and out of the element in the radial direction by conduction,

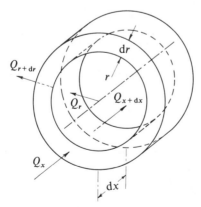

Fig. 6.9. Element of laminar flow in a tube.

and in the axial direction by convection. Conduction into the element is

$$Q_r = -k2\pi r \, dx \frac{\partial t}{\partial r}$$

Over the change of radius dr, this conduction rate will change by

$$\frac{\partial Q_r}{\partial r} dr = -k2\pi \, dx \frac{\partial}{\partial r}\left(r\frac{\partial t}{\partial r}\right) dr \qquad (6.20)$$

This change in conduction rate is accounted for by the difference between the convection rates into and out of the element in the axial direction. The axial velocity through the element is constant but the temperature changes in the axial direction. The rate of convection into the element is

$$2\pi r \, dr \, \rho v c_p t$$

and out of the element, it is

$$2\pi r \, dr \, \rho v c_p\left(t + \frac{\partial t}{\partial x} dx\right)$$

Hence, the difference is

$$2\pi r \, dr \, \rho v c_p \frac{\partial t}{\partial x} dx$$

The sum of this and the right-hand side of (6.20) is zero, hence on cancelling terms,

$$\frac{1}{vr}\frac{\partial}{\partial r}\left(r\frac{\partial t}{\partial r}\right) = \frac{\rho c_p}{k}\frac{\partial t}{\partial x} \qquad (6.21)$$

This is the energy equation for laminar flow in a tube. With a constant wall heat flux q_w, and constant fluid properties, the temperature of the fluid (at any radius) must increase linearly in the direction of flow, so that

$$\frac{\partial t}{\partial x} = \text{constant}$$

Other conditions applicable are that at $r = 0$, (tube axis), $\partial t/\partial r = 0$ and at $r = r_w$, $t = t_w$. Also at $r = r_w$, the heat flux is related to the temperature gradient,

$$q_w = -k\left(\frac{\partial t}{\partial r}\right)_{r_w}$$

Since $\partial t/\partial x$ is assumed constant, equation (6.21) reduces to a total differential equation. The velocity v is a function of the velocity at the axis of the tube, v_a, and the radius r. The assumed parabolic velocity distribution, equation (6.2), expressed in terms of r measured from the axis is

$$\frac{v}{v_a} = 1 - \left(\frac{r}{r_w}\right)^2$$

where r_w is the wall radius.

This result must be substituted into equation (6.21) before integrating. Hence, after re-arrangement,

$$\frac{\partial}{\partial r}\left(r\frac{\partial t}{\partial r}\right) = \frac{1}{\alpha}\frac{\partial t}{\partial x}v_a\left[1 - \left(\frac{r}{r_w}\right)^2\right]r$$

This is integrated to give

$$r\frac{\partial t}{\partial r} = \frac{1}{\alpha}\frac{\partial t}{\partial x}v_a\left(\frac{r^2}{2} - \frac{r^4}{4r_w^2}\right) + C_1$$

and after a second integration, gives

$$t = \frac{1}{\alpha}\frac{\partial t}{\partial x}v_a\left(\frac{r^2}{4} - \frac{r^4}{16r_w^2}\right) + C_1\ln r + C_2 \qquad (6.22)$$

C_1 and C_2 are constants of integration to be found from boundary conditions. Since $\partial t/\partial r = 0$ at $r = 0$, it follows that $C_1 = 0$. The other boundary condition is that at $r = r_w$, $t = t_w$. Hence,

$$t_w = \frac{1}{\alpha}\frac{\partial t}{\partial x}v_a\left[\frac{r_w^2}{4} - \frac{r_w^2}{16}\right] + C_2$$

$$\therefore \quad C_2 = t_w - \frac{1}{\alpha}\frac{\partial t}{\partial x}v_a\frac{3r_w^2}{16}$$

Hence equation (6.22) becomes, after some re-arrangement,

$$t = \frac{1}{\alpha}\frac{\partial t}{\partial x}v_a r_w^2\left[\frac{1}{4}\left(\frac{r}{r_w}\right)^2 - \frac{1}{16}\left(\frac{r}{r_w}\right)^4 - \frac{3}{16}\right] + t_w \qquad (6.23)$$

This equation may be expressed as a temperature difference, $\theta = t - t_w$. Further, if θ_a is the temperature difference between the axis, where $r = 0$, and the wall, θ_a may be found from equation

(6.23) by putting $r = 0$. Hence,

$$\theta_a = \frac{1}{\alpha}\frac{\partial t}{\partial x}v_a r_w^2\left(-\frac{3}{16}\right) \tag{6.24}$$

The temperature profile may be expressed non-dimensionally by dividing equation (6.23) by equation (6.24).

$$\therefore \quad \frac{\theta}{\theta_a} = 1 - \frac{4}{3}\left(\frac{r}{r_w}\right)^2 + \frac{1}{3}\left(\frac{r}{r_w}\right)^4 \tag{6.25}$$

The equation for heat transfer at the wall may be obtained by considering the temperature gradient at $r = r_w$. Thus, from equation (6.25)

$$\left(\frac{d\theta}{dr}\right)_{r_w} = \theta_a\left(-\frac{8}{3r_w} + \frac{4}{3r_w}\right) = -\frac{4\theta_a}{3r_w}$$

and

$$q_w = -k\left(\frac{d\theta}{dr}\right)_{r_w} = \frac{4k\theta_a}{3r_w} = h\theta_a$$

$$\therefore \quad h = \frac{4k}{3r_w}$$

In terms of the Nusselt number, Nu_d

$$Nu_d = \frac{hd}{k} = \frac{4k}{3r_w}\frac{2r_w}{k} = \frac{8}{3} \tag{6.26}$$

This value of Nusselt number is based on the difference in temperature between the tube axis and the wall. However, from a practical point of view it is more convenient to consider the difference in temperature between the bulk value and the wall. The bulk temperature is the mean temperature of the fluid, and the temperature difference required is given by

$$\theta_m = \frac{\displaystyle\int_0^{r_w} 2\pi r\,dr\rho v c_p\theta}{\displaystyle\int_0^{r_w} 2\pi r\,dr\rho v c_p}$$

Introducing equations for v and θ, this becomes

$$\theta_m = \frac{\displaystyle\int_0^{r_w} 2\pi\rho c_p v_a \theta_a \left[1 - \left(\frac{r}{r_w}\right)^2\right]\left[1 - \frac{4}{3}\left(\frac{r}{r_w}\right)^2 + \frac{1}{3}\left(\frac{r}{r_w}\right)^4\right] r\,dr}{\displaystyle\int_0^{r_w} 2\pi\rho c_p v_a \left[1 - \left(\frac{r}{r_w}\right)^2\right] r\,dr}$$

This, on integration, gives $\theta_m = \frac{44}{72}\theta_a$.
The heat transfer at the wall is,

$$q_w = -k\left(\frac{d\theta}{dr}\right)_{r_w} = \frac{4k\theta_a}{3r_w} = \frac{4k}{3r_w}\cdot\frac{72}{44}\theta_m$$

This is now equivalent to

$$q_w = h\theta_m$$

Hence

$$h = \frac{4k}{3r_w}\cdot\frac{72}{44}$$

and

$$\begin{aligned}
Nu_d = \frac{hd}{k} &= \frac{4k}{3r_w}\cdot\frac{72}{44}\cdot\frac{2r_w}{k} \\
&= \frac{8}{3}\cdot\frac{72}{44} \\
&= 4\cdot36
\end{aligned} \tag{6.27}$$

These results are independent of Reynolds number because, for fully developed flow, the boundary layer thickness is equal to the tube radius.

PROBLEMS

1. Derive the heat flow equation of the boundary layer

$$\frac{d}{dx}\int_0^l (\theta_s - \theta)U\,dy = \alpha\left(\frac{d\theta}{dy}\right)_0$$

and apply this equation to 'slug' flow of a liquid metal along a plate of uniform temperature to find the thickness of the temperature boundary layer. θ would be the liquid metal temperature relative to the plate temperature. Assume that the temperature profile in the boundary layer can be described by an equation of the form

$$\theta = a \sin\left[b\left(\frac{y}{\delta_t}\right) + c \right]$$

where a, b, and c are constants to be determined from the boundary conditions.

Hence prove that the local Nusselt number N_x is given by

$$N_x = \sqrt{\left(\frac{\pi - 2}{4}\right)}\sqrt{(R_x P)} = 0.534\sqrt{(R_x P)}$$

It can be shown that if the velocity profile can be approximated by an equation of the form

$$U = d \sin\left[e\left(\frac{y}{\delta}\right) + f \right]$$

the velocity boundary layer thickness is then given by

$$\frac{\delta}{x} = \sqrt{\left[\frac{2\pi^2}{(4 - \pi)R_x} \right]}$$

Show that for a liquid metal of $P = 0.01$ the temperature boundary layer thickness is approximately equal to 6δ. (*University of Bristol*).

2. Prove that, in hydrodynamically fully-developed laminar flow through a tube, the temperature field is determined by the following partial differential equation

$$\frac{1}{Ur}\frac{\partial}{\partial r}\left(r\frac{\partial t}{\partial r} \right) = \frac{1}{\alpha}\left(\frac{\partial t}{\partial x} \right)$$

where r is the distance from the axis of the tube, and U is the velocity at r.

Hence derive an equation for the fully developed temperature profile, when the heat flux q_w is constant along the wall of the tube. You may assume that the velocity profile is given by

$$\frac{U}{U_0} = 1 - \left(\frac{r}{R}\right)^2$$

Show that the temperature profile can be put into dimensionless form as

$$\frac{t - t_w}{t_0 - t_w} = \frac{\theta}{\theta_0} = 1 - \frac{4}{3}\left(\frac{r}{R}\right)^2 + \frac{1}{3}\left(\frac{r}{R}\right)^4$$

where t, t_0, and t_w are the local, axial, and wall temperatures respectively, and R is the radius of the tube. Also show that the Nusselt number

$$\frac{q_w d}{\theta_0 k} = \frac{8}{3}$$

Explain, by writing down the initial equations, how you would derive the Nusselt number $q_w d/\theta_m k$, where θ_m is the bulk temperature of the fluid relative to the wall. (*University of Bristol*).

3. Deduce a formula for the temperature profile in low speed laminar pipe flow which is at a temperature different from that of the pipe wall. Hence deduce the heat flow per unit area of the pipe wall. (*University of Oxford*).

4. The velocity in the boundary layer of a stream of air flowing over a flat plate can be represented by

$$\frac{u}{U} = \frac{3}{2}\left(\frac{y}{\delta}\right) - \frac{1}{2}\left(\frac{y}{\delta}\right)^3$$

where U is the main stream velocity, u the velocity at a distance y from the flat plate within the boundary layer of thickness δ. The variation of boundary layer thickness along the plate may be taken as

$$\delta/x = 4.64(Re_x)^{-\frac{1}{2}}$$

If the plate is heated to maintain its surface at constant temperature show that the average Nusselt number over a distance x from the leading edge of the hot plate is

$$Nu = 0.66(Pr)^{\frac{1}{3}}(Re_x)^{\frac{1}{2}}$$

(*University of Leeds*).

REFERENCES

1. Prandtl, L., and Tietjens, O. *Hydro- und Aeromechanik*, Vol. 2, 28, Berlin (1931). See also translated works in Dover Publications, New York (1934).
2. Knudsen, J. G., and Katz, D. L. *Fluid Dynamics and Heat Transfer*, McGraw-Hill, Inc., New York (1958).
3. Kármán, T. von, *Z. angew. Math. u. Mech.*, Vol. 1, 233 (1921).
4. Eckert, E. R. G., and Drake, R. M. *Heat and Mass Transfer*, 2nd ed., McGraw-Hill Book Company, Inc., New York (1959).
5. Pohlhausen, K. *Z. angew. Math. u. Mech.*, Vol. 1, 252 (1921).

7

Forced convection: Reynolds analogy and dimensional analysis

Consideration of convection has so far been limited to laminar flow. Different approaches are more suitable if the flow is turbulent.

7.1. Reynolds Analogy

The approach to forced convection known as Reynolds analogy is based on similarities between the equations for heat transfer and shear stress, or momentum transfer. The original ideas were due to Reynolds[1,2] and the analogy has been subsequently modified and extended by others.

The equation for shear stress in laminar flow, (6.4), may be written as

$$\tau = \rho v \frac{dv}{dy} \tag{7.1}$$

A similar equation may be written for shear stress in turbulent flow. A term ε, eddy diffusivity, is introduced, which enables the shear stress due to random turbulent motion to be written

$$\tau_t = \rho \varepsilon \frac{dv}{dy} \tag{7.2}$$

When turbulent flow exists, a molecular shear stress is also present which may be added to τ_t. The total shear stress in turbulent flow is thus

$$\tau = \rho(v + \varepsilon) \frac{dv}{dy} \tag{7.3}$$

ε is not a property of the fluid as v is. It depends on several factors such as the Reynolds number of the flow and the turbulence level. Its value is generally many times greater than v.

94

7.1.1. Shear Stress at the Solid Surface. In developing Reynolds analogy the heat transfer at the surface of a flat plate or of a tube is ultimately compared with the shear stress acting at that surface. This shear stress is obtained by substituting $(dv/dy)_{y=0}$ into the equation for τ. Thus, for laminar flow on a flat plate, x from the leading edge,

$$Cf = \frac{0.647}{Re_x^{\frac{1}{2}}} \qquad (7.4)$$

where Cf is the skin friction coefficient defined as $\tau_w/\frac{1}{2}\rho v_s^2$. v_s is the free stream velocity. An average value Cd acting over the whole length up to x is found to be $2Cf$, where Cf is the local value at x. The derivative of the turbulent velocity profile substituted into (7.2) leads to an infinite shear stress at the wall. This is overcome by assuming the existence of a laminar sub-layer, as in Fig. 6.1. For turbulent flow on a flat plate, Cf and Cd are given by

$$Cf = 0.0583(Re_x)^{-\frac{1}{5}} \qquad (7.5)$$

and

$$Cd = \frac{0.455}{(\log Re_x)^{2.58}} \qquad (7.6)$$

Equation (7.6) is an empirical relationship,[3] which takes into account the laminar and turbulent portions of the boundary layer.

The ratio of the velocity at the limit of the laminar sublayer to the free stream velocity is also of importance, as will be seen later; this is a function of the Reynolds number at x from the leading edge:

$$\frac{v_b}{v_s} = \frac{2.12}{(Re_x)^{0.1}} \qquad (7.7)$$

Corresponding relationships for flow in tubes are usually expressed in terms of a friction factor f, which is four times larger than Cf in terms of the surface shear stress. Thus $f = 4\tau_w/\frac{1}{2}\rho v_m^2$, where v_m is the mean velocity of flow

$$\text{In laminar flow,} \qquad f = \frac{64}{Re_d} \qquad (7.8)$$

$$\text{and in turbulent flow,} \qquad f = \frac{0.308}{(Re_d)^{\frac{1}{4}}} \qquad (7.9)$$

and

$$\frac{v_b}{v_m} = \frac{2\cdot44}{(Re_d)^{\frac{1}{8}}} \qquad (7.10)$$

The derivations of these relationships may be found in the more advanced texts on heat transfer, or fluid mechanics, e.g., refs. 4, 14.

The friction factors quoted above are for smooth surfaces. Values are increased if the surface is rough. For any *tube* surface, the average wall shear stress τ_w acting over a length L can be found by considering the forces acting. Thus, if Δp is the pressure loss and d the tube diameter, the pressure force $\Delta p \pi d^2/4$ is equal to the wall shear force $\tau_w \pi dL$, assuming the tube is horizontal.

7.1.2. Heat Transfer across the Boundary Layer. Equations for heat transfer across the boundary layer are written in analogous form to (7.1) and (7.3). Thus in laminar flow, heat transfer *across* the flow can only be by conduction, so Fourier's law may be written as

$$q = \rho c_p \alpha \frac{dt}{dy} \qquad (7.11)$$

In turbulent conditions energy will also be carried across the flow by random turbulent motion, and the heat flux may be written

$$q = \rho c_p (\alpha + \varepsilon_q) \frac{dt}{dy} \qquad (7.12)$$

where ε_q is the thermal eddy diffusivity, a term analogous to ε. The basis of Reynolds analogy is to compare equations (7.1) and (7.11) for laminar flow, and equations (7.3) and (7.12) for turbulent flow.

Some initial assumptions must now be made. The first is that $\varepsilon = \varepsilon_q$. This means that if an eddy of fluid, at a certain temperature and possessing a certain velocity, is transferred to a region at a different state, then it assumes its new temperature and velocity in equal times. This assumption is found by experiment to be approximately true. ($\varepsilon_q/\varepsilon$ varies between 1 and 1·6. For a review of this subject, see ref. 4.) A second assumption is that q and τ have the same ratio at all values of y. This will be true when velocity and temperature profiles are identical. Identical profiles occur in laminar flow when the Prandtl number of the fluid is 1. In turbulent flow, with $\varepsilon = \varepsilon_q$, the groups responsible for velocity and temperature distributions, $(v + \varepsilon)$ and $(\alpha + \varepsilon_q)$, are also equal when

$Pr = 1$. Further, even when the Prandtl number is not 1, $(v + \varepsilon)$ and $(\alpha + \varepsilon_q)$ will be nearly equal, since ε and ε_q are very much greater than v and α.

The simple Reynolds analogy is valid when $Pr = 1$, and the Prandtl–Taylor modification[5,6] which takes into account a varying Pr is valid for a fairly restricted range, say $0.5 < Pr < 2.0$.

7.1.3. The Simple Reynolds Analogy.

With the assumptions noted above it is now possible to proceed to a consideration of the simple analogy. Flow is assumed to be either all laminar or all turbulent, and $Pr = 1$. By comparing equations (7.1) and (7.11) for laminar flow, it follows that

$$\frac{q}{\tau} = \frac{k}{\mu} \frac{dt}{dv} \tag{7.13}$$

This gives the ratio of q/τ at some arbitrary plane in the flow. Noting that q/τ has the same value anywhere in the y-direction, it is possible to express q_w/τ_w at the wall in terms of free stream and wall temperatures and velocities.

Thus

$$\frac{q_w}{\tau_w} = \frac{k}{\mu} \frac{(t_s - t_w)}{v_s} \tag{7.14}$$

Details of the nomenclature are shown in Fig. 7.1. v_w at the wall is zero.

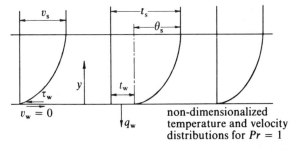

non-dimensionalized temperature and velocity distributions for $Pr = 1$

Fig. 7.1. *Velocity and temperature distributions for the simple Reynolds analogy.*

For turbulent flow, equations (7.3) and (7.12) give

$$\frac{q}{\tau} = \frac{\rho c_p (\alpha + \varepsilon_q) \, dt}{\rho (v + \varepsilon) \, dv}$$

Thus, between the free stream and wall:

$$\frac{q_w}{\tau_w} = c_p \frac{(t_s - t_w)}{v_s} \qquad (7.15)$$

Equations (7.14) and (7.15) for laminar and turbulent flow are clearly identical if $Pr = 1$, i.e., if $c_p = k/\mu$, or $\mu c_p/k = 1$. Re-arranging equation (7.15) gives

$$h = \frac{q_w}{\theta_s} = \frac{\tau_w c_p}{v_s}$$

where $\theta_s = (t_s - t_w)$, and where h is the surface heat transfer coefficient.

Substituting the skin friction coefficient Cf gives

$$h = \frac{Cf}{2} \rho v_s c_p$$

or

$$\frac{h}{\rho v_s c_p} = \frac{Cf}{2} \qquad (7.16)$$

This is one form of the result obtained from the simple Reynolds analogy; it gives the convection coefficient h in terms of the skin friction coefficient Cf. $h/\rho v_s c_p$ is the Stanton number St. It is the Nusselt number divided by the product of the Reynolds and Prandtl numbers. Further re-arrangement is possible; for example, considering laminar flow at distance x from the leading edge of a flat plate, both sides of (7.16) are multiplied by x/k to give

$$\frac{hx}{k} = \frac{Cf}{2} \frac{\rho v_s x c_p}{k}$$

But $c_p \mu/k = 1$, or $c_p/k = 1/\mu$, hence

$$\frac{hx}{k} = \frac{Cf}{2} \frac{\rho v_s x}{\mu}$$

or

$$Nu_x = \frac{Cf}{2} Re_x \qquad (7.17)$$

Cf may be replaced by $0.647(Re_x)^{-\frac{1}{2}}$ from equation (7.4) to give

$$Nu_x = 0.323(Re_x)^{\frac{1}{2}} \qquad (7.18)$$

for laminar flow on a flat plate. This result may be compared with equation (6.18) obtained by consideration of the integral boundary layer equations. If $Pr = 1$ in this equation then the result is

$$Nu_x = 0.332(Re_x)^{\frac{1}{2}}$$

Reynolds analogy may also be applied to flow in tubes, and for this purpose θ_s and v_s in the above analysis may be replaced by the mean values θ_m and v_m, since the velocity and temperature distributions are identical. The linear dimension is now the diameter of the tube, d. The relationship will be

$$\frac{hd}{k} = \frac{Cf}{2} \frac{\rho v_m d}{\mu}$$

or

$$Nu_d = \frac{Cf}{2} Re_d \tag{7.19}$$

For turbulent flow in tubes, $f = 0.308(Re_d)^{-\frac{1}{4}}$ from (7.9) and $Cf = \frac{1}{4}f$ from the definition of f. Substituting for Cf in (7.19) gives

$$Nu_d = 0.038(Re_d)^{0.75} \tag{7.20}$$

7.1.4. The Prandtl–Taylor Modification of Reynolds Analogy. The simple Reynolds analogy agreed quite well with experiment in laminar flow and also with results where $Pr = 1$ in both laminar and turbulent flow. The modification proposed by Prandtl and Taylor goes a long way to meeting the discrepancies generally found in turbulent flow when there is no restriction on Pr. A laminar sublayer is considered in addition to the turbulent boundary layer. This makes an important difference to the analysis even though the sublayer is quite thin. The fact that it is thin is also important in that it makes it possible to assume a linear temperature and velocity distribution with negligible error.

For turbulent heat and momentum exchange between the free stream and the laminar sublayer, as in Fig. 7.2, applying equation (7.15) gives:

$$\frac{q_b}{\tau_b} = \frac{c_p(t_s - t_b)}{(v_s - v_b)} \tag{7.21}$$

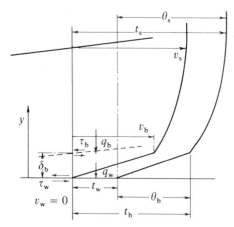

Fig. 7.2. *Velocity and temperature distributions for the Prandtl–Taylor modification of Reynolds analogy.*

In the laminar sublayer, the equations are

$$q_w = \frac{k(t_b - t_w)}{\delta_b}$$

and

$$\tau_w = \frac{\mu v_b}{\delta_b}$$

and hence

$$\frac{q_w}{\tau_w} = \frac{k(t_b - t_w)}{\mu v_b} \tag{7.22}$$

Because the velocity and temperature distributions are straight lines in the laminar region $q_w = q_b$, and $\tau_w = \tau_b$. Hence the right-hand sides of (7.21) and (7.22) are equal.

$$\therefore \quad \frac{c_p(t_s - t_b)}{v_s - v_b} = \frac{k}{\mu} \frac{(t_b - t_w)}{v_b}$$

and

$$\frac{Pr(t_s - t_b)}{(t_b - t_w)} = \frac{v_s - v_b}{v_b}$$

If $(t_s - t_w)$ is written as θ_s, then the above may be re-arranged to give

$$\frac{(t_b - t_w)}{\theta_s} \frac{v_s}{v_b} = \frac{Pr}{1 + \frac{v_b}{v_s}(Pr - 1)}$$

and eliminating $(t_b - t_w)/v_b$ between this result and equation (7.22) gives

$$\frac{q_w}{\tau_w} = \frac{k\theta_s}{\mu v_s} \cdot \frac{Pr}{1 + \dfrac{v_b}{v_s}(Pr - 1)}$$

$$\therefore \quad \frac{q_w}{\tau_w} = c_p \frac{\theta_s}{v_s} \frac{1}{1 + \dfrac{v_b}{v_s}(Pr - 1)} \tag{7.23}$$

This equation is Reynolds analogy as modified by Prandtl and Taylor. It may be noted straight away that if $Pr = 1$ in this equation, then the relationship reduces to equation (7.15), i.e., Reynolds original equation. Further, if $v_b = 0$, i.e., there is no laminar sub-layer so that flow is entirely turbulent, the equation again reduces to the original relationship. A further simplification is that if flow is all laminar, which means that $v_b = v_s$, equation (7.23) becomes

$$\frac{q_w}{\tau_w} = \frac{c_p \theta_s}{v_s Pr} = \frac{k\theta_s}{v_s \mu}$$

Equation (7.23) may now be treated in a similar manner to (7.15) by re-arranging and introducing the coefficient Cf. Thus:

$$\frac{q_w}{\theta_s} = \rho v_s c_p \frac{Cf}{2} \frac{1}{1 + \dfrac{v_b}{v_s}(Pr - 1)} \tag{7.24}$$

For turbulent flow on flat plates, both sides are multiplied by x/k and μ is introduced to the right-hand side to give

$$\frac{q_w x}{\theta_s k} = \frac{\rho v_s x}{\mu} \frac{c_p \mu}{k} \frac{Cf}{2} \cdot \frac{1}{1 + \dfrac{v_b}{v_s}(Pr - 1)}$$

$$\therefore \quad Nu_x = \frac{Cf}{2} \frac{Re_x Pr}{1 + \dfrac{v_b}{v_s}(Pr - 1)}$$

Also, for turbulent flow on flat plates, equations (7.5) and (7.7) are introduced to give

$$Nu_x = \frac{0 \cdot 0292 Re_x^{\frac{4}{5}} Pr}{1 + 2 \cdot 12 Re_x^{-\frac{1}{10}}(Pr - 1)} \tag{7.25}$$

This is the local Nusselt number. To obtain an average Nusselt number over some total length of plate, Cd from equation (7.6) may be substituted for Cf in this analysis.

An alternative to this result was suggested by Colburn,[7] in which the denominator in equation (7.25) was replaced by $Pr^{\frac{2}{3}}$. Rearranged, this gives

$$St_x Pr^{\frac{2}{3}} = 0{\cdot}0292 Re_x^{-0{\cdot}2} \qquad (7.26)$$

and if Cf is substituted, this gives

$$St_x Pr^{\frac{2}{3}} = \frac{Cf}{2} = J, \qquad \text{(the Colburn J-factor)} \qquad (7.27)$$

This result reduces to equation (7.16) when $Pr = 1$.

For turbulent flow in round tubes, equation (7.23) may be suitably modified. θ_s becomes θ_m, the temperature difference between the mean fluid temperature and the wall, and v_s similarly becomes v_m. Introducing k, μ, and the linear dimension d, gives

$$\frac{q_w d}{\theta_m k} = \frac{\rho v_m d}{\mu} \frac{c_p \mu}{k} \cdot \frac{Cf}{2} \cdot \frac{1}{1 + \dfrac{v_b}{v_m}(Pr - 1)}$$

$$\therefore \quad Nu_d = \frac{Cf}{2} \cdot \frac{Re_d Pr}{1 + \dfrac{v_b}{v_m}(Pr - 1)}$$

Finally, equations (7.9) and (7.10) are introduced to eliminate Cf and v_b/v_m, and remembering that $f = 4Cf$, the result obtained is

$$\overline{Nu_d} = \frac{0{\cdot}0386 Re_d^{\frac{3}{4}} Pr}{1 + 2{\cdot}44 Re_d^{-\frac{1}{4}}(Pr - 1)} \qquad (7.28)$$

This is an average Nusselt number, because an average friction factor was used.

The relationships (7.25) and (7.28) agree remarkably well with experiment over a small range of Prandtl number.

EXAMPLE 7.1

Compare the heat transfer coefficients for water flowing at an average fluid temperature of 100°C, and at a velocity of 0·232 m/s in a 2·54 cm bore pipe, using the simple Reynolds analogy, equation

(7.20), and the Prandtl–Taylor modification, equation (7.28). At $100°C$, $Pr = 1.74$, $k = 0.68$ W/m deg C, and $v = 0.0294 \times 10^{-5}$ m^2/s.

Solution. The Reynolds number is:

$$\frac{vd}{v} = \frac{0.232 \times 0.0254 \times 10^5}{0.0294} = 20,000$$

In the simple analogy, $\overline{Nu_d} = 0.038Re_d^{0.75}$, and $Re_d^{0.75} = 1643$

$$\therefore \quad \overline{Nu_d} = 62.5, \quad \text{and} \quad \bar{h} = \frac{62.5 \times 0.68}{0.0254}$$

$$= 1675 \text{ W/m}^2 \text{ deg C}$$

In the Prandtl–Taylor modification,

$$\overline{Nu_d} = \frac{0.0386Re_d^{0.75}Pr}{1 + 2.44(Re_d)^{-\frac{1}{8}}(Pr - 1)}$$

$$Re_d^{\frac{1}{8}} = 3.45$$

$$\therefore \quad \overline{Nu_d} = \frac{0.0386 \times 1643 \times 1.74}{1 + (2.44/3.45) \times 0.74} = 72.4$$

$$\therefore \quad \bar{h} = \frac{72.4 \times 0.68}{0.0254} = 1937 \text{ W/m}^2 \text{ deg C.}$$

The first answer is thus 13.5 per cent lower than the second, which may be assumed more correct. This solution is for flow in smooth pipes.

7.2. Dimensional Analysis of Forced Convection

Convection heat transfer is an example of the type of problem which is difficult to approach analytically, but which may be solved more readily by dimensional analysis and experiment.

The process of dimensional analysis enables an equation to be written down which relates important physical quantities, such as flow velocity and fluid properties, in dimensionless groups. The precise functional relationship between these dimensionless groups is determined by experiment.

Suppose that in a given process there are n physical variables which are relevant. These variables, which may be denoted by $Q_1, Q_2, \ldots, Q_n$, are composed of k independent dimensional quantities such as mass, length, and time. Buckingham's pi theorem[8] states that if a dimensionally homogeneous equation relating the variables may be written, then it may be replaced by a relationship of $(n - k)$ dimensionless groups.

Thus, if

$$\phi_1(Q_1, Q_2, \ldots, Q_n) = 0$$

then

$$\phi_2(\pi_1, \pi_2, \ldots, \pi_{(n-k)}) = 0$$

Each π term will be composed of the Q variables, in the general form

$$\pi = Q_1^a Q_2^b Q_3^c \ldots Q_n^x,$$

and will be dimensionless. The set of π terms will include all independent dimensionless groupings of the variables. No π term can be formed by combining other π terms. A set of equations for $a, b, c, \ldots, x$ is obtained by equating the sum of the exponents of each independent dimension to zero. This will yield k equations for n unknowns. One method of solution is to choose values for $(n - k)$ of the exponents in each term. The selected exponents must be independent, which can be shown to be true if the determinant formed from the coefficients of the others does not vanish.

An alternative procedure is to select k of the Q variables and to combine them in turn with each of the other $(n - k)$ Q variables. The selection k of the Q quantities must together involve all the independent dimensions, but they must not form a dimensionless group by themselves. Further, each of the $(n - k)$ Q variables in each π term is given the exponent 1. This facilitates the algebra, as will be seen, and is allowable since it only amounts to reducing the π term by some unknown root. Thus, if there were six Q variables and four independent dimensions, the two π terms would be:

$$\pi_1 = Q_1^{a_1} Q_2^{b_1} Q_3^{c_1} Q_4^{d_1} Q_5$$

$$\pi_2 = Q_1^{a_2} Q_2^{b_2} Q_3^{c_2} Q_4^{d_2} Q_6$$

In each π term there are therefore four simultaneous equations for the four unknown exponents.

This procedure will now be applied to forced convection. For a detailed mathematical proof of the pi theorem, the reader is referred to Langhaar.[9]

The physical variables are the convection coefficient h, a characteristic velocity v, a linear dimension l, and the fluid properties conductivity k, viscosity μ, specific heat c_p, and density ρ. In flow along a flat plate, the velocity is the free stream value and the linear dimension is the distance from the leading edge. In pipe flow, the velocity is the mean value and the linear dimension is the diameter.

The independent dimensional quantities to be used are mass M, length L, time T, temperature θ, and heat H. Heat, of course, is not independent as it has the same dimensions as kinetic energy, ML^2/T^2, but for present purposes it can be regarded as independent provided there is no transference of energy from one form to another. Heating effects due to fluid friction are consequently neglected, and the results are invalid for high speed flow. Inspection of the dimensions of the physical variables shows that when the dimensions of H and θ occur, (in h, k, and c_p), they do so in the same combination of H/θ. Thus H/θ can be regarded as an independent dimensional quantity.

In forced convection there are therefore seven physical variables involving four dimensional quantities. Consequently, three π terms will be obtained. Four variables which together involve all four dimensions, and which do not themselves form a dimensionless group, are v, l, k, and μ. Then h, c_p, and ρ will each appear in a separate independent π term. The π terms are

$$\pi_1 = v^{a_1} l^{b_1} k^{c_1} \mu^{d_1} h$$

$$\pi_2 = v^{a_2} l^{b_2} k^{c_2} \mu^{d_2} c_p$$

$$\pi_3 = v^{a_3} l^{b_3} k^{c_3} \mu^{d_3} \rho$$

The π_1 term may be written

$$\left(\frac{L}{T}\right)^{a_1} \left(L\right)^{b_1} \left(\frac{H}{LT\theta}\right)^{c_1} \left(\frac{M}{LT}\right)^{d_1} \frac{H}{L^2 T \theta} = 1$$

since it is dimensionless. The following equations for a_1, b_1, c_1, and d_1 are obtained:

$$L \quad : \quad a_1 + b_1 - c_1 - d_1 - 2 = 0$$

$$T \quad : \quad -a_1 - c_1 - d_1 - 1 = 0$$

$$H/\theta \quad : \quad c_1 + 1 = 0$$

$$M \quad : \quad d_1 = 0$$

It is found that $a_1 = 0$, $b_1 = 1$, $c_1 = -1$, and $d_1 = 0$. The π_1 term is thus hl/k. In a similar manner, it is found that the π_2 term is $\mu c_p/k$ and the π_3 term $\rho v l/\mu$. These groups are recognized as the Nusselt, Prandtl, and Reynolds numbers, and the result may be expressed:

$$\phi_2(Nu, Pr, Re) = 0$$

or, more usually,

$$Nu = \phi(Re, Pr) \qquad (7.29)$$

since the Nusselt number contains the dependent variable h. Equation (7.29) agrees in form with Reynolds analogy, in that the Nusselt number is a function of the Reynolds and Prandtl numbers. Actual functional relationships have been determined for various fluids, geometries, and flow regimes; these may be used to predict h in similar circumstances, provided the Reynolds and Prandtl numbers fall within the same ranges. There is, of course, no restriction to the system of *units* which may be used, provided they are consistent.

Scale model testing is a valuable practical application of the use of these dimensionless relationships. By means of experiments on a model, the performance of a projected design may be estimated. The requirements are that the model must be geometrically similar to the full scale design; also that Reynolds and Prandtl numbers must be reproduced exactly. Then the flow patterns and fluid and thermal boundary layers will be correctly modelled and, consequently, the Nusselt number determined on the model will be the correct value for the real thing.

Some of the more useful results will now be summarized. It should be pointed out first, however, that the dimensional analysis just considered was based on the assumption of constant fluid properties and also that a single linear dimension was sufficient to describe the system. Both of these assumptions are invalid in certain circumstances. Viscosity is often the most temperature dependent fluid property, and a varying viscosity will have a considerable effect on the fluid boundary layer. If this is allowed for in the dimensional analysis, an additional term, such as a viscosity ratio to some power, will appear. In a result of the form of equation (7.29), fluid property values at some mean temperature are used. Consequently, when these equations are used to predict heat transfer coefficients, property values at the appropriate mean temperature must be inserted. For pipe flow, an average or mean fluid temperature is used. If the flow across a certain section of pipe were to be thoroughly mixed, then an average fluid temperature would be obtained. It will depend on the velocity profile as well as the temperature profile. To evaluate an average heat transfer coefficient over a length of pipe, then property values at a mean of the average temperatures at the two ends must be inserted. When flow over a flat plate is being considered, a mean film temperature may be used. This is the average of the free stream fluid temperatures and the wall temperature. In addition, an average of two mean film temperatures may be used when considering an average convection coefficient over a length of plate.

When an additional linear dimension is required, as in the case of thermal boundary layer development in pipe flow, a length ratio to some power will appear in the analysis.

7.3. Empirical Relationships for Forced Convection

Some of the more important relationships are now listed.

Laminar flow in tubes, distance x from entry.

$$Nu_d = 1.86(Re_d)^{\frac{1}{3}}(Pr)^{\frac{1}{3}}\left(\frac{d}{x}\right)^{\frac{1}{3}}\left(\frac{\mu}{\mu_w}\right)^{0.14}, \text{(ref. 10)} \quad (7.30)$$

An average Nusselt number is given by:

$$\overline{Nu_d} = 3.65 + \frac{0.0668(d/x)Re_dPr}{1 + 0.04[(d/x)Re_dPr]^{\frac{2}{3}}}, \text{(ref. 11)} \quad (7.31)$$

These results are valid for $0.5 < Pr < 100$.

Turbulent flow in tubes, for liquids and gases of low Prandtl number:

$$\overline{Nu_d} = 0.023(Re_d)^{\frac{4}{5}}(Pr)^{\frac{2}{5}}, \text{(ref. 12)} \quad (7.32)$$

A wider range of Prandtl number is covered by the following pair of equations:

$$\text{heating fluid, } \overline{Nu_d} = 0.0243(Re_d)^{\frac{4}{5}}(Pr)^{\frac{2}{5}}, \text{(ref. 13)} \quad (7.33)$$

$$\text{cooling fluid, } \overline{Nu_d} = 0.0265(Re_d)^{\frac{4}{5}}(Pr)^{\frac{3}{10}} \quad (7.34)$$

For appreciably viscous fluids:

$$\overline{Nu}_d = 0 \cdot 027(Re_d)^{\frac{4}{5}}(Pr)^{\frac{1}{3}}\left(\frac{\mu}{\mu_w}\right)^{0 \cdot 14}, \text{(ref. 10)} \qquad (7.35)$$

Turbulent flow along flat plates

$$\overline{Nu}_x = 0 \cdot 036 Pr^{\frac{1}{3}}(Re_x^{\frac{4}{5}} - 18,700), \text{(ref. 14)} \qquad (7.36)$$

Fluids of very low Prandtl number. For sodium–potassium alloys, with both uniform wall temperatures and uniform heat flux, in tubes,

$$\overline{Nu}_d = 6 \cdot 27 + 0 \cdot 00514(Re_d Pr)^{1 \cdot 0}, \text{(ref. 15)} \qquad (7.37)$$

The temperature profile becomes very peaked compared with the velocity profile, when the Prandtl number is very small, as shown in Fig. 7.3.

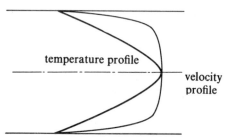

Fig. 7.3. *Non-dimensionalized temperature and velocity profiles for flow in a tube at very low values of Pr.*

EXAMPLE 7.2

Compare equations (7.32), (7.34), and (7.35) to obtain the Nusselt number for oil flowing in a cooler. The oil has an average fluid temperature of 80°C, ($Pr = 490$, $k = 0 \cdot 139$ W/m deg C, $\mu = 0 \cdot 0319$ N s/m^2) and the tube wall temperature is maintained at 38°C ($\mu = 0 \cdot 212$ N s/m^2). The Reynolds number is 5000.

Solution. Equation (7.32), $\overline{Nu}_d = 0 \cdot 023(Re_d)^{\frac{4}{5}}(Pr)^{\frac{2}{5}}$, is not expected to be accurate in this case. The result is

$$\overline{Nu}_d = 0 \cdot 023 \times 903 \cdot 7 \times 11 \cdot 91 = 248$$

Equation (7.34), $\overline{Nu_d} = 0.0265(Re_d)^{\frac{4}{5}}(Pr)^{\frac{3}{10}}$, gives

$$\overline{Nu_d} = 0.0265 \times 903.7 \times 6.41 = 153.6$$

Equation (7.35), $\overline{Nu_d} = 0.027(Re_d)^{\frac{4}{5}}(Pr)^{\frac{1}{3}}(\mu/\mu_w)^{0.14}$, gives

$$\overline{Nu_d} = 0.027 \times 903.7 \times 7.89 \times (0.0319/0.212)^{0.14} = 147.6$$

PROBLEMS

1. The expression, Stanton number $= \frac{1}{2} \times$ friction factor, may be derived from the simple Reynolds analogy. Briefly explain this analogy, discussing any assumptions made and stating limitations to the application of the above expression.

Air at a mean pressure of 100 lbf/in^2 and a mean temperature of 150°F flows through a pipe of 2 in. internal diameter at a mean velocity of 20 ft/s. The inner surface of the pipe is maintained at a constant temperature and the pressure drop along a 30 ft length of pipe is 7.90 lbf/ft^2. Determine: (a) the Stanton number, and (b) the mean surface heat transfer coefficient. (Ans. 0.002, 15.3 Btu/ft^2 h deg F.) (*University of London*).

2. Deduce the Taylor–Prandtl equation

$$\frac{H}{F} = \frac{c\theta}{\mu}\left[\frac{1}{1 + a(Pr - 1)}\right]$$

which gives the heat transfer per unit area and time, H, in terms of the drag force per unit area, F, and in which Pr denotes the Prandtl number $c\mu/k$; the other symbols having their usual meaning. ($a = v_b/v_s$.)

Use the Taylor–Prandtl equation to show mathematically the following deductions, and explain them in simple terms:

(a) For gases the Taylor–Prandtl equation approximates closely to the Reynolds equation. (Reynolds equation is $\dfrac{H}{F} = \dfrac{c\theta}{v}$ but for liquids the divergence is considerable.)

(b) For turbulent flow the Taylor–Prandtl equation reduces to the Reynolds equation but for streamline flow it reduces to $\dfrac{H}{F} = \dfrac{k\theta}{\mu v}$.

(c) If the value of the Prandtl number is unity, then the form of the Taylor–Prandtl equation for streamline and turbulent conditions is identical.

(d) With liquids of very low thermal conductivity, the whole of the temperature drop occurs in the boundary layer. (*King's College, London*).

3. Discuss the effects of boundary layers on heat transfer by convection, and show that, if Reynolds analogy between friction and heat transfer applies,

$$\frac{h}{c_p\rho\bar{u}} = \frac{f}{2}.$$

It was found during a test in which water flowed with a velocity of 2·44 m/s through a tube 2·54 cm inside diameter and 6·08 m long, that the head lost due to friction was 1·22 m of water. Estimate the surface heat transfer coefficient, based on the above analogy. For water $\rho = 998$ kg/m^3, $c_p = 4187$ J/kg deg C. (Ans. 21,400 J/m^2 s deg C.) (*Queen Mary College, London*).

4. Air at a temperature of 115·6°C enters a smooth pipe 7·62 cm diameter, the wall of which can be maintained at a constant temperature of 15·6°C. The rate of flow of air is 0·0226 m^3/sec. Estimate the length of pipe necessary if the air is to be cooled to 65·5°C, using the following assumptions: Prandtl number for air = 0·74; $f = 0·007$; velocity at boundary of sublayer is half the mean velocity in the pipe. (Ans. 12·55 m.) (*University College, London*).

5. Explain what is meant by the term 'Nusselt number'. Why are dimensionless quantities of particular importance in convective heat transfer?

A portion of the air intake of an aircraft engine is to be electrically heated to prevent icing. It is desired to establish what heat input will be necessary to give a prescribed temperature difference between intake and air at a flight speed of 500 ft/s at an altitude of 40,000 ft.

Tests are carried out on a quarter-scale model in a wind-tunnel operating at atmospheric pressure. The air and surface temperatures are those of the flight condition. Calculate

(*a*) the necessary air speed upstream of the model in the tunnel for similarity between the model and the flight conditions; and

(*b*) the necessary heat input in flight if that in the model is 10 kW.

Notes: (i) At 40,000 ft altitude the atmospheric pressure is 0·185 atm. (ii) The kinematic viscosity of air is inversely proportional to pressure. (iii) The thermal conductivity of air is independent of pressure. (Ans. 370 ft/sec, 40 kW.) (*Imperial College, London*).

6. Using dimensional analysis of a convective heat transfer system derive an expression for the Nusselt number in terms of the Prandtl and Reynolds numbers.

Oil at 30°C flows through a 1·2 cm diameter pipe at 75 cm/s. The physical properties in c.g.s. units for the oil at this temperature are:

$$c_p = 0·4, \quad \mu = 5 \times 10^{-3}, \quad k = 0·355 \times 10^{-3}, \quad \rho = 0·90$$

Determine the temperature and velocity of water flowing through a $\frac{3}{4}$ in. diameter pipe in order that Reynolds and Prandtl numbers should be equal to those pertaining to the above oil flow system.

If the surface heat transfer coefficient for the water flow is found to be 630 Btu/h ft^2 deg F, calculate the surface coefficient for the oil flow, justifying briefly the basis of the method. (Ans. 84·3°F, 2·34 ft/s, 0·033 gcal/cm^2 s deg C.) (*University of Manchester*).

7. (*a*) Describe the following dimensionless quantities used in the study of heat transfer: *Nu, Re, Pr, Gr, St*, giving their physical interpretations in a form of simple ratios.

(b) Describe, using suitable formulae, what is known as Reynolds analogy. Show that under certain conditions,

$$St = 2\tau/\rho v^2$$

(See also chapter 8.) (*University of Oxford*).

8. Air at mean conditions of 510°C, 101·3 kN/m², and 6·09 m/s flows through a thin 2·54 cm diameter copper tube in surroundings at 272°C.
(a) At what rate, per metre length, will the tube lose heat?
(b) What would be the reduction of heat loss if 2·54 cm of lagging with $k = 0·173$ J/m s deg C were applied to the tube? Take $N_d = 0·023(R_d)^{0·8} P^{0·33}$ with all the properties taken at the bulk air temperature. Assume the surface heat transfer coefficient from the outside of the unlagged and lagged tube to be 17·0 and 11·3 J/m² s deg C respectively. (Ans. 174 J/ms, 32 per cent.) (*University of Bristol*).

9. Estimate the heat transfer coefficient for xylene flowing through a circular pipe diameter 1·5 cm with velocity 100 cm/s. Properties of xylene may be taken to be:
Specific heat, c_p 0·41 cal/g deg C
Viscosity, μ 0·005 g/cm s
Thermal conductivity, k 0·00035 cal/cm s deg C
Density, ρ 0·88 g/cm³
The estimate is to be based on figures for water flowing through a ¾ in. diameter pipe which show that the heat transfer coefficient

$$h = 150(1 + 0·011t)\frac{v^{0·8}}{d^{0·2}} \text{ Btu/h ft}^2 \text{ deg F}$$

where t is the average water temperature in deg F, v is velocity in ft/s, and d is the pipe diameter in inches.
The properties of water are given in the following table, all in ft lb h deg F units:

t	c_p	μ	k	ρ
60	0·999	2·73	0·34	62·34
70	0·998	2·37	0·347	62·27
80	0·997	2·09	0·353	62·11

(Ans. 0·0365 cal/cm³ s deg C.) (*University of Leeds*).

10. Explain and derive the simple Reynolds analogy between heat transfer and fluid friction. Outline the Prandtl–Taylor modification to the simple theory.
19,800 lb/h of air is to be heated from 15 to 75°C using a shell and tube heat exchanger. The tubes which are 1·25 in. in diameter have condensing steam on the outside and the tube wall temperature may be taken as 100°C. Specify the number of tubes in parallel and their length if the maximum allowable pressure drop is 5 in. of water.

Assume that $f = 0.079Re^{-\frac{1}{4}}$ and that the air has the following properties: density 0.07 lb/ft^3, kinematic viscosity $1.86 \times 10^{-4} \text{ ft}^2/\text{s}$. (To solve this problem, see also chapter 13.) (Ans. 94 tubes, 12·3 ft long.) (*University of Leeds*).

References

1. Reynolds, O. *Proc. Manchester Lit. Phil. Soc.*, Vol. 14, 7 (1874).
2. Reynolds, O. *Trans. Roy. Soc. Lond.*, Vol. 174A, 935 (1883).
3. Schlichting, H. *Boundary Layer Theory*, McGraw-Hill Book Company, Inc., New York (1955).
4. Knudsen, J. G., and Katz, D. L. *Fluid Dynamics and Heat Transfer*, McGraw-Hill Book Company, Inc., New York (1958).
5. Prandtl, L. *Z. Physik.*, Vol. 11, 1072 (1910).
6. Taylor, G. I. *British Adv. Comm. Aero., Reports and Mem.*, Vol. 274, 423 (1916).
7. Colburn, A. P. *Trans. AIChE*, Vol. 29, 174 (1933).
8. Buckingham, E. *Phys. Rev.*, Vol. 4, 345 (1914).
9. Langhaar, H. L. *Dimensional Analysis and Theory of Models*, John Wiley, New York (1951).
10. Sieder, E. N., and Tate, G. E. *Ind. Eng. Chem.*, Vol. 28, 1429 (1936).
11. Hausen, H. *Z. V. D. I., Beih. Verfahrenstech.*, No. 4, 91 (1943).
12. McAdams, W. H. *Heat Transmission*, 3rd ed., McGraw-Hill Book Company, Inc., New York (1954).
13. Dittus, F. W., and Boelter, L. M. K. *University of California Publ. Eng.*, Vol. 2, 443 (1930).
14. Chapman, A. J. *Heat Transfer*, 1st ed., The Macmillan Company, New York (1960).
15. Baker, R. A., and Sesonske, A. *Nuclear Science and Engineering*, Vol. 13, 283 (1962).

8

Natural convection

Forced convection heat transfer has now been considered in some detail. The energy exchange between a body and an essentially stagnant fluid surrounding it is another important example of convection. Fluid motion is due entirely to buoyancy forces arising from density variations in the fluid. There is often slight motion present from other causes; any effects of these random disturbances must be assumed negligible in an analysis of the process. Natural convection is generally to be found when any object is dissipating energy to its surroundings. This may be intentional, in the essential cooling of some machine or electrical device, or in the heating of a house or room by a convective heating system. It may also be unintentional, in the loss of energy from a steam pipe, or in the dissipation of warmth to the cold air outside the window of a room.

Fluid motion generated by natural convection may be laminar or turbulent. The boundary layer produced now has zero fluid velocity at both the solid surface and at the outer limit, and the profile is of the form shown in Fig. 8.1. In laminar flow natural convection

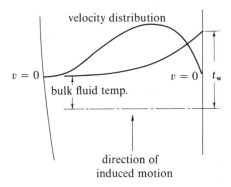

Fig. 8.1. Natural convection boundary layer on a vertical flat plate.

113

from a vertical plate, it is possible to obtain a solution of the boundary layer equations of motion and energy, if a body force term is included. This approach is limited in general application and, consequently, the method of dimensional analysis will be used.

8.1. The Body Force

Before undertaking a dimensional analysis of natural convection it is necessary to consider the nature of the body force. If ρ_s is the density of cold undistorbed fluid, ρ is the density of warmer fluid, and θ is the temperature difference between the two fluid regions, then the buoyancy force on unit volume is

$$(\rho_s - \rho)g$$

and ρ_s is related to ρ by

$$\rho_s = \rho(1 + \beta\theta)$$

where β is the coefficient of cubical expansion of the fluid. Thus the buoyancy force is

$$[\rho(1 + \beta\theta) - \rho]g = \rho g\beta\theta \qquad (8.1)$$

The independent variables on which natural convection depends may now be listed. Fluid properties are ρ, μ, c_p, and k. Properties of the particular problem are the characteristic linear dimension, l, and the overall temperature difference θ. Fluid flow depends on the buoyancy force given by equation (8.1). θ and ρ have already been listed, thus it is only necessary to add βg. In most cases, variation of g is unlikely.

8.2. Dimensional Analysis of Natural Convection

The procedure outlined in chapter 7 will now be followed to obtain the dimensionless groups relevant to natural convection. There are eight physical variables and five dimensional quantities, so that three π terms are expected. H and θ may not be combined to form a single dimensional quantity, since temperature difference is now an important physical variable.

Five physical variables selected to be common to all π terms are ρ, μ, k, θ, and l. These fulfil the necessary conditions. h, c_p, and βg

will each appear in a separate π term. The π terms are:

$$\pi_1 = \rho^{a_1}\mu^{b_1}k^{c_1}\theta^{d_1}l^{e_1}h$$

$$\pi_2 = \rho^{a_2}\mu^{b_2}k^{c_2}\theta^{d_2}l^{e_2}c_p$$

$$\pi_3 = \rho^{a_3}\mu^{b_3}k^{c_3}\theta^{d_3}l^{e_3}\beta g$$

After writing the necessary equations to obtain the exponents a to e in each π term, it is found that

$$\pi_1 = \frac{hl}{k}; \quad \pi_2 = \frac{\mu c_p}{k}; \quad \pi_3 = \frac{\beta g\theta\rho^2 l^3}{\mu^2}$$

The π_3 term is the Grashof number and the dimensionless relationship may be expressed as

$$\phi(Nu, Pr, Gr) = 0$$

or,

$$Nu = \phi(Gr, Pr) \tag{8.2}$$

The Grashof number is a dimensionless group in natural convection which is equivalent to Reynolds number in forced convection. $\beta g\rho\theta$ is the buoyancy force on unit volume, so that the force on unit area is $\beta g\rho\theta l$. This is equivalent to shear stress $\mu v/l$. If the group $\beta g\rho\theta l$ in the Grashof number is replaced by $\mu v/l$, the result is $(\mu v/l)(\rho l^2/\mu^2)$, which is $(\rho v l/\mu)$, the Reynolds number.

Many experiments have been performed to establish the functional relationships for different geometric configurations convecting to various fluids. Generally, it is found that equation (8.2) is of the form

$$Nu = a(GrPr)^b \tag{8.2a}$$

where a and b are constants. The product $GrPr$ is the Rayleigh number Ra. However, results are generally quoted in terms of $(GrPr)$ since it is often necessary to vary Gr at some fixed Pr. Laminar and turbulent flow regimes have been observed in natural convection, and transition generally occurs in the range $10^7 < GrPr < 10^9$ depending on the geometry.

8.3. Formulae for the Prediction of Natural Convection

Some of the more important results obtained will now be presented. These may be used for design calculations provided the system under consideration is geometrically similar and that the value of $(GrPr)$ falls within the limits specified. Generally, there are no restrictions on the use of any specific fluid. Example 8.1 shows how the formulae are used. Figure 8.2 shows the principal geometries. For more extensive reviews of available information see, for example, refs. 2 and 3.

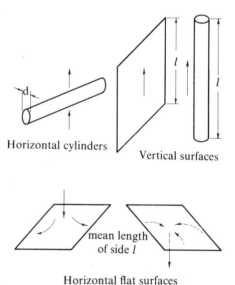

Horizontal cylinders

Vertical surfaces

mean length of side l

Horizontal flat surfaces

Fig. 8.2. *Principal geometries in natural convection systems showing direction of convective flow.*

8.3.1. Horizontal Cylinders. Detailed measurements indicate that the convection coefficient varies with angular position round a horizontal cylinder, but for design purposes values given by the following equations[1] are constant over the whole surface area, for cylinders of diameter d.

$$\overline{Nu}_d = 0.525(Gr_dPr)^{0.25} \qquad (8.3)$$

when $10^4 < Gr_dPr < 10^9$ (laminar flow) and

$$\overline{Nu}_d = 0.129(Gr_dPr)^{0.33} \qquad (8.4)$$

when $10^9 < Gr_dPr < 10^{12}$ (turbulent flow). Below $Gr_dPr = 10^4$, it is not possible to express results by a simple relationship, and ultimately the Nusselt number decreases to a value of 0·4. At these low values of Gr_dPr the boundary layer thickness becomes appreciable in comparison with the cylinder diameter, and in the case of very fine wires heat transfer occurs in the limit by conduction through a stagnant film. Fluid properties are evaluated at the average of the surface and bulk fluid temperatures, which is the mean film temperature. If the surface temperature is unknown, a trial and error solution is necessary to find h from a known heat transfer rate.

8.3.2. Vertical Surfaces. Both vertical flat surfaces and vertical cylinders may be considered using the same correlations of experimental data. The characteristic linear dimension is the length, or height, of the surface, l. This follows from the fact that the boundary layer results from vertical motion of fluid and the length of boundary layer is important rather than its width. Again average values of Nu_l are given, even though in the case of $Gr_lPr > 10^9$ the boundary layer is initially laminar and then turbulent. With physical constants at the mean film temperature the numerical constants as recommended by McAdams[1] are

$$\overline{Nu}_l = 0·59(Gr_lPr)^{0·25} \qquad (8.5)$$

when $10^4 < Gr_lPr < 10^9$ (laminar flow) and

$$\overline{Nu}_l = 0·129(Gr_lPr)^{0·33} \qquad (8.6)$$

when $10^9 < Gr_lPr < 10^{12}$ (turbulent flow).

8.3.3. Horizontal Flat Surfaces. Fluid flow is most restricted in the case of horizontal surfaces, and the size of the surface has some bearing on the experimental data. The heat transfer coefficient is likely to be more variable over a smaller flat surface than a large one, when flow effects at the edges become less significant. Further, there will be a difference depending on whether the horizontal surface is above or below the fluid. Similar, though reversed, processes take place for hot surfaces facing upwards (i.e., cold fluid *above* a hot surface), and cold surfaces facing downwards (i.e., hot fluid *below* a cold surface). In either case, the fluid is relatively free to move due to buoyancy effects and be replaced by fresh fluid entering at the edges. Fishenden and Saunders[2] recommend the following for square or rectangular horizontal surfaces up to a mean length of side (l) of 2 ft:

$$\overline{Nu}_l = 0.54(Gr_lPr)^{0.25} \tag{8.7}$$

when $10^5 < Gr_lPr < 10^8$ (laminar flow) and

$$\overline{Nu}_l = 0.14(Gr_lPr)^{0.33} \tag{8.8}$$

when $Gr_lPr > 10^8$ (turbulent flow). Thus turbulent flow is possible in this geometrical arrangement.

The converse arrangement is the hot surface above a cold fluid, or hot surface facing downwards, and a hot fluid above a cold surface, or cold surface facing upwards. In either case, it is obvious that convective motion is severely restricted since the surface itself prevents vertical movement. Laminar motion only has been observed, and the recommendation is

$$\overline{Nu}_l = 0.25(Gr_lPr)^{0.25} \tag{8.9}$$

when $Gr_lPr > 10^5$. Fluid properties are again taken at the mean film temperature.

8.3.4. Approximate Formulae for use with Air. A great deal of natural convection work involves air as the fluid medium and the fluid properties of air do not vary greatly over limited temperature ranges. Thus it is possible to derive simple formulae from equations (8.3) to (8.9) in which the physical properties in the Nusselt, Grashof, and Prandtl numbers are grouped together and assumed constant. From equation (8.2a)

$$h = \text{constant}\left[k^{1-b}\left(\frac{\beta g\rho^2 c_p}{\mu}\right)^b\right]\theta^b l^{3b-1}$$

$$= \text{constant} \times \theta^b l^{3b-1} \tag{8.10}$$

It will have been noted that $b = 0.25$ in laminar flow and 0.33 in turbulent flow, so that the index of l is -0.25 in laminar flow and 0 in turbulent flow. The simplified expressions become

$$h = C\left(\frac{\theta}{l}\right)^{0.25} \quad \text{in laminar flow} \tag{8.11}$$

and

$$h = C\theta^{0.33} \quad \text{in turbulent flow} \tag{8.12}$$

where the value of C, the constant, depends on the configuration and flow, and l is the characteristic dimension.

The resulting expressions for horizontal cylinders, vertical and horizontal surfaces, as given by McAdams,[1] are:

Horizontal cylinders
d = diameter

$$h = 0.27\left(\frac{\theta}{d}\right)^{0.25} \qquad \text{laminar flow}$$

$$h = 0.18\theta^{0.33} \qquad \text{turbulent flow}$$

Vertical surfaces
l = height

$$h = 0.29\left(\frac{\theta}{l}\right)^{0.25} \qquad \text{laminar flow}$$

$$h = 0.19\theta^{0.33} \qquad \text{turbulent flow}$$

Horizontal surfaces
l = length of side

Hot, facing upwards
Cold, facing downwards

$$h = 0.27\left(\frac{\theta}{l}\right)^{0.25} \qquad \text{laminar flow}$$

$$h = 0.22\theta^{0.33} \qquad \text{turbulent flow}$$

Hot, facing downwards
Cold, facing upwards

$$h = 0.12\left(\frac{\theta}{l}\right)^{0.25} \qquad \text{laminar flow}$$

These equations must only be used with Btu, ft, h, deg F units. It must not be expected that these formulae will give answers as accurate as the previously quoted equations. To determine whether the flow is laminar or turbulent it is necessary to evaluate the approximate value of $(GrPr)$. For this purpose it may be assumed that the value of $\beta g\rho^2 c_p/\mu k$ is 10^6. This has then to be multiplied by (linear dimension)$^3 \times \theta$ ft^3 deg F, to obtain the product $(GrPr)$.

EXAMPLE 8.1

An oil filled electric heating panel has the form of a thin vertical rectangle, 5 ft long by 2 ft 6 in. high. It convects freely from both surfaces. The surface temperature is 170°F and the surrounding air temperature 68°F. Calculate the rate of heat transfer by natural convection, and compare the result with that obtained from the simplified formula for air.

Fluid properties at the average of surface and bulk air temperatures, 119°F, are $\beta = 1/579$, $Pr = 0.701$, $\rho = 0.0685$, $\mu = 0.0472$, and $k = 0.0161$, in ft, lb, h, deg F units.

Solution. The characteristic linear dimension is the panel height, 2·5 ft. To evaluate the product $(Gr_l Pr)$ consistent units must be used. All property values quoted are in the correct units. Note, however, that g, the gravitational acceleration is $32·2 \times 60^4$ ft/h². Hence:

$$(Gr_l Pr) = \frac{1 \times 32·2 \times 60^4 \times 102 \times 0·0685^2 \times 2·5^3 \times 0·701}{579 \times 0·0472^2}$$

$$= 1·70 \times 10^9$$

Hence, flow is turbulent.

Using equation (8.6), $\overline{Nu}_l = 0·129(Gr_l Pr)^{0·33}$

$$\therefore \quad h = \frac{0·0161 \times 0·129 \times 1111·2}{2·5} = 0·924 \text{ Btu/ft}^2 \text{ h deg F}$$

$$\therefore \quad Q = 0·924 \times 2(5 \times 2·5) \times 102 = 2354 \text{ Btu/h}$$

The corresponding simple formula for air is $h = 0·19\theta^{0·33}$

$$\therefore \quad h = 0·19 \times (102)^{0·33}$$

$$= 0·19 \times 4·6$$

$$= 0·873 \text{ Btu/ft}^2 \text{ h deg F}$$

$$\therefore \quad Q = 0·873 \times 2(5 \times 2·5) \times 102 = 2224 \text{ Btu/h}$$

The difference is $130/2354 = 5·53$ per cent. The use of the simplified formula is consequently justified.

PROBLEMS

1. Describe briefly how experimental data on heat transfer by convection obtained from small scale experiments may be applied to full-scale industrial plant, and specify the conditions which must be satisfied for this to be possible.

Define the Nusselt, Prandtl, and Grashof numbers and show that they are dimensionless. Calculate the rate of heat transfer by natural convection from the outside surface of a horizontal pipe of 6 in. outside diameter and 20 ft long. The surface temperature of the pipe is 180°F and that of the surrounding air 60°F.

The following relations are applicable to heat transfer by natural convection to air from a horizontal cylinder; for laminar flow, when $10^4 < (GrPr) < 10^9$

$$Nu = 0·56(GrPr)^{\frac{1}{4}}$$

and for turbulent flow, when $10^9 < (GrPr) < 10^{12}$

$$Nu = 0·12(GrPr)^{\frac{1}{3}}$$

The properties of air given below, corresponding to the 'mean film tempera-ture', i.e., 120°F, may be used.

Kinematic viscosity $v = 0.700 \text{ ft}^2/\text{h}$

Thermal conductivity $k = 0.0164 \text{ Btu/ft h deg R}$

Coefficient of cubical expansion $\beta = \dfrac{1}{580}(\text{deg R})^{-1}$

Prandtl number $Pr = 0.701$. (Ans. 4350 Btu/h.) (Queen Mary College, London).

2. The transfer of heat by natural convection from vertical planes may be calculated by using the following formula which is valid for all P, for R less than 10^9 and for N greater than 5.

$$N^4/R = 2P/(5 + 10P^{\frac{1}{2}} + 10P)$$

where $N = \dot{Q}''L/k\theta$,
$\quad\quad R = (\Delta\rho)gL^3\rho c_p/\mu k$,
$\quad\quad P = \mu c_p/k$,
and where

L = height of plane, $\quad\quad\quad\quad\quad\quad k$ = thermal conductivity
θ = temperature difference, $\quad\quad\quad\quad g$ = gravitational acceleration
c_p = isobaric specific heat-capacity
μ = viscosity, $\quad\quad\quad\quad\quad\quad\quad\quad \rho$ = density,
$(\Delta\rho)$ = difference between density of fluid near plane and density of fluid far away,
$\dot{Q}''$ = surface density of rate of heat transfer.

Some busbars are in the form of strips which run horizontally and are ten times as high as they are thick. They are made of copper for which the resistivity is 2×10^{-6} ohm centimetre.

They are to be designed for operation at 87·8°C in an atmosphere which is at 32·2°C and at 101·3 kN/m². Calculate the height of busbar for use with a current of 10,000 A. Assume that both radiation and that part of the convec-tion which is from the top and bottom edges of the bars are negligible. (Ans. 0·35 m.) (Queen Mary College, London).

3. By dimensional analysis show that for natural convection of a perfect gas

$$\frac{hl}{k} = f\left\{\left(\frac{l^3g}{v^2}\right),\left(\frac{T_s - T_0}{T_0}\right),\left(\frac{\mu c_p}{k}\right)\right\} = f(GrPr)$$

where v is the kinematic viscosity, T_s is the surface temperature and T_0 is the temperature in the bulk of the fluid. Give a brief statement of the assump-tions made.

A metal plate, 0·609 m in height, forms the vertical wall of an oven and is at a temperature of 171°C. Within the oven is air at a temperature of 93·4°C and atmospheric pressure. Assuming that natural convection conditions hold near the plate, and that for this case $Nu = 0.548(GrPr)^{0.25}$, find the mean heat transfer coefficient, and the heat taken up by the air per second, per metre width. For air at 132·2°C, $k = 0.0322$ J/m s deg C, $\mu = 0.232 \times 10^{-4}$ kg/ms. (Ans. 4·11 J/m² s deg C, 195 J/m s.) (Queen Mary College, London).

4. A flat vertical plate loses heat by natural convection. The thickness of the boundary layer (δ) at any height (x) from the bottom of the plate is obtained from the equation

$$\frac{\delta}{x} = 3\cdot93(Pr)^{-\frac{1}{2}}(0\cdot952 + Pr)^{\frac{1}{4}}(Gr_x)^{-\frac{1}{4}}$$

where Pr is the Prandtl number and Gr_x the Grashof number $\left(\dfrac{g\beta\Delta Tx^3}{v^2}\right)$.

By assuming a laminar flow with a parabolic velocity distribution obtain an expression for the convection loss from the plate.

A nominal 6 in. steam pipe is covered with 2 in. of insulation and mounted horizontally. The inner surface of the pipe has a temperature of 200°F and the ambient air is at 70°F. Calculate the surface temperature and the rate of heat loss per foot run of pipe assuming that this occurs by natural convection only.

The following may be useful:

Pipe outside diameter	6·63 in.
Pipe inside diameter	6·07 in.
Pipe conductivity	27 Btu/h ft deg F
Insulation conductivity	0·04 Btu/h ft deg F

For natural convection with $10^9 > GrPr > 10^4$, $h = 0\cdot27(\Delta t/D)^{\frac{1}{4}}$ and for $GrPr > 10^9$, $h = 0\cdot18(\Delta t)^{\frac{1}{3}}$.

Assume that air has the following properties:

$\rho = 0\cdot0678$ lb/ft³ $\mu = 0\cdot0476$ lb/ft h
$k = 0\cdot0163$ Btu/h ft deg F, $Pr = 0\cdot7$.

(Ans. 99·5°F, 53·3 Btu/ft h.) (*University of Leeds*).

REFERENCES

1. McAdams, W. H. *Heat Transmission*, 3rd ed., McGraw-Hill Book Company, Inc., New York (1954).

2. Fishenden, M., and Saunders, O. A. *An Introduction to Heat Transfer*, Oxford University Press (1950).

3. Hsu, S. T. *Engineering Heat Transfer*, D. Van Nostrand Company, Inc., Princeton (1963).

9

Separated flow convection

Separation is an important characteristic of the type of flow encountered in many modern heat transfer devices. Design requirements of compactness have resulted in the rapid growth of the use of complex geometrical heat transfer surfaces, which have developed from the single tube and tube bank placed across the line of flow. A single tube or cylinder placed in a cross-flow is completely submerged in the fluid and it therefore forms an obstacle around which the fluid must flow. A boundary layer exists on the cylindrical surface with free stream velocity at its extreme and zero velocity at the wall. However, the free stream velocity increases around the front of the cylinder and at low approach velocities flow within the boundary layer also accelerates. Behind the cylinder free stream and boundary layer flow decelerates again in a more or less reverse pattern. At higher approach velocities the increased velocity around the front of the cylinder which is accompanied by a drop in static pressure is not followed by a similar increase in velocity in the boundary layer, due to the increased viscous stress at the higher velocity gradients. Thus, in the boundary layer the fluid has lost velocity before it starts to decelerate behind the cylinder and it is then opposed by a 'surplus' of static pressure which forces the boundary layer away from the surface. Separation, or break-away, results in the formation of turbulent eddies which are carried downstream behind the cylinder. Separation occurs nearer the front of the cylinder as the approach velocity increases, and occurs much more readily in flow over blunt ended obstacles.

Local heat transfer coefficients have been measured around the circumference of cylinders in cross-flow.[1] They have minimum values at the point of separation and increase forwards towards the point of stagnation, but they increase more towards the rear of the cylinder. This may be attributed to the scrubbing action of the eddies formed in that vicinity. Average values of heat transfer coefficient have also been extensively determined as these are required for design purposes. Owing to the degree of turbulence produced in a tube bank, convection coefficients are high and average values for tubes several rows back are found to be higher than for those at entry due to the action of eddies shed from the leading rows.[2]

The pattern of events in the tube bank has led to the evolution of the compact heat transfer surface which is in general a complex of finned cross-flow passages. The use of fins as a means of increasing heat transfer coefficients is discussed in chapter 12. Flow through such a system is largely composed of turbulent eddies, and even at low approach velocities a high degree of turbulence is to be found. For this reason the usual transition between laminar and turbulent flow at Reynolds numbers around 2500 does not exist, and turbulent flow has been found to persist to Reynolds numbers as low as 800.[3]

In any arrangement of this type in which high heat transfer rates may be obtained in a small space, the advantages have to be balanced against the effect of increased pressure loss on overall performance. Pressure loss is due to the total drag of the shapes involved and due to shear over the fins. It may be measured across the whole system and related to a friction coefficient by an expression similar to the equation for flow in pipes:

$$\Delta p = f_D \frac{L}{d} \rho \frac{v_m^2}{2} \qquad (9.1)$$

Such a form is useful since it has been found generally that f_D can be related to the Reynolds number of flow. In the determination of f_D from Δp, the values of L, d, and v_m have to be defined in relation to the particular geometry. The symbol f_D is used to indicate that it represents essentially a drag loss rather than a loss due to viscous shear.

9.1. Relationship between Heat Transfer and Pressure Loss in a Complex Flow System

It will be apparent that the performance of heat transfer surfaces of the type under consideration can only be determined by experiment. This means extensive, and often expensive testing of different designs to determine an optimum heat transfer performance when set against the unavoidable pressure loss. An approach by Schenck[4] enables the heat transfer performance to be predicted from pressure loss measurements, which is a simpler measurement to make. Using a wide variety of experimental information, the Colburn J-factor was plotted against f_D as defined above in equation (9.1). Since the J-factor is a function of Reynolds number, as is the friction coefficient, it would be reasonable to expect some relationship between the J-factor and f_D. The result is shown in Fig. 9.1. f_D was based on the hydraulic radius of the flow passages, and it is seen that there

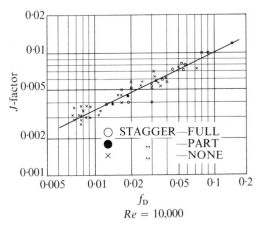

Fig. 9.1. Relationship between the J-factor and f_D for flow in a complex system. By courtesy of H. Schenck, Jr., and The American Society of Naval Engineers, Inc.

is a correlation between heat transfer and frictional drag for the surfaces studied which included plain fins on tubes, plain and dimpled tubes, tube and spiral fins, flattened tubes with plain grooved and wavy fins, pin fins and interrupted plate fins. This particular plot holds for Reynolds numbers in excess of 5000; below this figure separate curves are needed for different Reynolds number ranges.

This result is interesting in that it may be regarded as indicating that an 'experimental analogy' exists between heat transfer and friction in complex flow arrangements, when the net friction effects involved are essentially due to drag forces.

The use of this information is illustrated in the following example.

EXAMPLE 9.1

A compact forced convection oil cooler has a frontal area of $1.5\,\text{ft}^2$ and a surface area of $40\,\text{ft}^2/\text{ft}^2$ frontal area. Air at $65°F$ enters the cooler at $80\,\text{ft/s}$. The average temperature of the heat transfer surface is $200°F$. f_D is found to be 0.1. Estimate the heat transfer performance.

Solution. From Fig. 9.1 the *J*-factor is 0.01. The *J*-factor is given by equation (7.27). At $200°F$, ρ for air is $0.0602\,\text{lb/ft}^3$, $c_p = 0.241\,\text{Btu/lb}$ deg F, $Pr = 0.693$. Hence, the heat transfer coefficient is given by

$$\frac{\bar{h} \times (0.693)^{\frac{2}{3}}}{0.0602 \times 80 \times 3600 \times 0.241} = 0.01$$

$$\therefore \quad \bar{h} = 53.3\,\text{Btu/ft}^2\,\text{h deg F}$$

The heat transfer rate is $\bar{h}A\theta\,\text{Btu/h}$,

$$= 53.3 \times 1.5 \times 40 \times (200 - 65)$$

$$= 432{,}000\,\text{Btu/h}.$$

9.2. Convection from a Single Cylinder in Cross Flow

Much experimental work has been done to determine the heat transfer coefficient from a single cylinder in cross flow. Investigations have included both fine heated wires and large pipes. A recent examination of available data is that of Douglas and Churchill[5] and the equation which represents their results is

$$\overline{Nu}_d = 0.46(Re_d)^{\frac{1}{2}} + 0.00128(Re_d) \tag{9.2}$$

This equation is only valid for $Re_d > 500$. Nusselt and Reynolds numbers are based on the cylinder diameter d, velocity is the free stream, or undisturbed fluid velocity, and fluid properties are evaluated at the average film temperature. Hsu[6] has proposed that for $Re_d < 500$ the following equation may be used:

$$\overline{Nu}_d = 0.43 + 0.48(Re_d)^{\frac{1}{2}} \tag{9.3}$$

Both of these equations are valid only for the simpler gases with similar Prandtl numbers, since the small Prandtl number effects are accommodated in the numerical constants. Both equations are valid in heating as well as cooling of the cylinder.

9.3. Convection in Flow across Tube Bundles

It is not possible here to say much about this topic, except that a great deal of experimental work has been done to find suitable empirical relationships for heat transfer coefficients. The reader is referred to volumes such as Kays and London[7] for extended coverage of the present situation.

In general, results correlate in the usual form, i.e., $\overline{Nu} = f(RePr)$, provided the characteristic dimension is expressed as some function of tube diameter and tube spacing. Various definitions have been proposed by different investigators. These results for average convection coefficients must be used with caution since local coefficients do not as a rule become constant until at least the third row of tubes in the bundle.

In addition to the heat transfer measurements, a great deal of work has been done to measure friction coefficients, expressible as functions of tube spacing and Reynolds number.

PROBLEMS

(To solve these problems see also chapter 13.)

1. A heat exchanger design method quotes the film coefficient of heat transfer for fluid flowing at right angles to staggered banks of tubes as:

$$h = 0.35vdc\left(\frac{k}{zcd}\right)^{0.7}\left(\frac{z}{Dv}\right)^{0.4}$$

where h = film coefficient, d = density of fluid, c = specific heat of fluid, z = kinematic viscosity, k = thermal conductivity of fluid, D = outside diameter of tubes, v = mean velocity of fluid across tubes, all in consistent units. Comment briefly on the validity of this expression from the theoretical viewpoint.

An organic liquid is condensed inside the horizontal tubes (1 in. o.d., staggered banks) of a heat exchanger by a flow of amyl alcohol through the shell, which is fitted with baffles such that the mean velocity of the amyl alcohol across the tubes is 4 ft/s. The vapour in the tubes condenses at 121°C with a latent heat of 111 cal/g, and heats the alcohol from 27 to 93°C. The film coefficient on the shell side is controlling. Calculate approximately the average quantity of condensate produced per hour per foot of tube.

For amyl alcohol: thermal conductivity, 0.09 Btu/h ft deg F; specific heat, 0.6 Btu/lb deg F; density, 51 lb/ft³, and viscosity (absolute), 2.2 cP. (Ans. 17.5 kg/h.) (*University of Leeds*).

2. A proposed 'economizer', for heating the feed water to a boiler, is to consist of a nest of vertical pipes, of 4 in. outside diameter, spaced at 7 in. centres across the flue; the tubes to be arranged in an 'in-line' form.

The boiler is to evaporate 10,000 lb/h with a fuel consumption of 1500 lb/h; the fuel and firing conditions being such that 30 lb of flue gases are produced per lb of fuel.

The flue is of square section of 4 ft 6 in. side, and the economizer is placed in an enlarged section 8 ft high and of width such that the velocity of the gases in the smallest passage between a pair of tubes is the same as the mean velocity in the flue.

The gases enter the economizer at 600°F and the feed water enters the tubes at 60°F.

The maximum pressure drop across the unit, which can be tolerated, is 0·15 in. of water.

Estimate the number of tubes across the flue, the number of rows of tubes in the direction of the gas flow, the exit temperature of the flue gases and of the feed water and the heat transferred per hour.

For a tube nest, with more than about four rows of tubes in the direction of the gas flow, and with either 'in-line' or 'staggered' arrangement of the tubes, the following equations for the heat transfer and the pressure drop are found to hold:

1. $$hd/k = 0{\cdot}33 C_h Re^{0{\cdot}6} Pr^{0{\cdot}33}$$

where Re is the Reynolds number based upon the tube diameter and Pr is the Prandtl number, and

2. $$P = 5{\cdot}2 \times 10^{-3} C_f n \rho v^2$$

where P is the pressure drop, in lb/ft^2, across the tube nest, ρ is the density of the gas and n is the number of rows of tubes in the direction of the gas flow.

In each case the velocity is that in the narrowest channel between the tubes and is in ft/s in the second formula.

For the purposes of the present problem, C_h and C_f may both be taken as unity, the temperature difference between the feed water and the surface of the tube and the temperature drop across the thickness of the tube wall may be neglected and the values of the various physical properties of the gas, in Btu/ft h deg F units, may be taken as follows:

$$c = 0{\cdot}25, \quad \mu = 0{\cdot}065, \quad \rho = 0{\cdot}044, \quad k = 0{\cdot}022$$

(Ans. 10, 13, 446°F, 233°F, 1,730,000 Btu/h.) (*Kings College, London*).

References

1. Schmidt, E., and Wenner, K. *Forschung, Gebiete Ingenieurw.*, Vol. 12, 65 (1933).
2. Snyder, N. W. *Chem. Eng. Progr.*, Symposium Series, Vol. 49, No. 5, 11 (1953).
3. Schenck, H. Jnr. *Heat Transfer Engineering*, Longmans, Green and Co. Ltd. (1960).
4. Schenck, H. Jnr. *J. Amer. Soc. Naval Eng.*, Vol. 69, 767 (1957).

5. Douglas, M. J. M., and Churchill, S. W. *Chem. Eng. Propr.*, Symposium Series, Vol. 52, No. 18, 23 (1956).
6. Hsu, S. T. *Engineering Heat Transfer*, D. Van Nostrand Company, Inc., Princeton (1963).
7. Kays, W. M., and London, A. L. *Compact Heat Exchangers*, McGraw-Hill Book Company, Inc., New York (1964).

10

Convection with phase change

Convection processes with phase change are of great importance, particularly those involving boiling and condensing in the fluid phase. Such processes occur in steam power plant and in chemical engineering plant. Convection in the liquid to solid phase change is also of importance, as for example in metallurgical processes, but this cannot be considered here.

10.1. Description of Condensing Flow

Two types of condensation are recognized, in which the condensing vapour forms either a continuous film of liquid on the solid surface, or a large number of droplets. Film condensation is the more common; drop formation occurs generally in an initial transient stage of condensing flow, or if for any reason the surface is unwettable. A condensing vapour generally forms droplets around nuclei of minute solid particles, and these droplets merge into a continuous film as they grow in number and size. The film then flows under the action of gravity so that the process may continue. As condensation depends on conduction of heat away through the solid surface, the growth of a liquid film will impede the condensation rate. Condensation is also impeded if a non-condensable gas is mixed with the vapour, since the concentration of gas tends to be greater at the surface as the vapour changes its phase, and this acts as a thermally insulating layer. It is thus desirable to prevent the film growing in thickness, and for this reason horizontal tubes are most commonly used as the condensing surface. Cold water flows inside the tube whilst the vapour condenses outside. The tubes are staggered vertically to prevent too great a build-up of film on the lower tubes as liquid drips off the upper ones. In comparison with the horizontal tube a vertical tube or flat surface will allow the liquid film to grow in thickness considerably, and the average heat transfer rate per unit area is somewhat smaller than for the horizontal tube.

10.2. A Theoretical Model of Condensing Flow

Nusselt proposed an analysis of condensation in 1916.[1] This was applied first to a vertical surface and the same mechanism was then extended to the horizontal tube. The results agree well with experiment. The analysis of the vertical surface will be given here to illustrate the method, and the reader may refer to the literature for the more lengthy analysis of the horizontal tube.[2,3]

Certain simplifying assumptions are made in the analysis. The film of liquid formed flows down the vertical surface under the action of gravity and flow is assumed everywhere laminar. Only viscous shear and gravitational forces are assumed to act on the fluid, thus inertial and normal viscous forces are neglected. Further, there is no viscous shear between the liquid and vapour phases, so there is no velocity gradient at the phase interface. (The temperature of the surface is assumed constant at t_w and the vapour is saturated at temperature $t_{sat.}$). The mass flow rate down the surface increases with distance from the top; this increase is associated with the amount of fluid condensing at any chosen point. The model to be considered is shown in Fig. 10.1. The velocity contour is of the form shown, with $v_x = 0$ at the surface, and $(\partial v_x/\partial y)_{y=\delta} = 0$ at the liquid–vapour interface.

Assuming that the vertical surface has unit width, it is necessary to consider an element of fluid $dx\, dy$ and unit depth, at a distance x from the top of the plate. The body force on this element is $\rho g\, dx\, dy$. The shear stress at y is

$$\tau_y = \mu\frac{dv_x}{dy}$$

The shear stress at $y + dy$ is

$$\tau_{y+dy} = \tau_y + \frac{d\tau_y}{dy}dy = \mu\frac{dv_x}{dy} + \mu\frac{d^2v_x}{dy^2}dy$$

These shear stresses act over an area $1 \times dx$. Balancing the forces

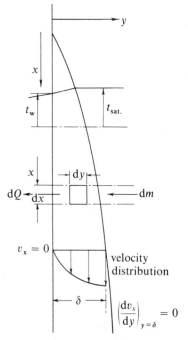

Fig. 10.1. *Condensation on a vertical surface.*

gives

$$\rho g \, dx \, dy = (\tau_y - \tau_{y+dy}) \, dx = -\mu \frac{d^2 v_x}{dy^2} \, dx \, dy$$

$$\therefore \quad \frac{d^2 v_x}{dy^2} = -\frac{\rho g}{\mu}$$

and on integration,

$$v_x = -\frac{\rho g y^2}{2\mu} + C_1 y + C_2$$

The boundary conditions are that $v_x = 0$ at $y = 0$ and $dv_x/dy = 0$ at $y = \delta$, the thickness of the film. Hence

$$C_2 = 0, \quad \text{and} \quad -\frac{\rho g \delta}{\mu} + C_1 = 0$$

The equation for v_x is thus

$$v_x = -\frac{\rho g}{\mu}\left(\frac{y^2}{2} - y\delta\right) \qquad (10.1)$$

The mass flow at x can then be obtained by integrating over the film thickness δ. Thus

$$m = \int_0^\delta \rho v_x \, dy = \int_0^\delta -\frac{\rho^2 g}{\mu}\left(\frac{y^2}{2} - y\delta\right) dy$$

$$= -\frac{\rho^2 g \delta^3}{6\mu} + \frac{\rho^2 g \delta^3}{2\mu} = \frac{\rho^2 g \delta^3}{3\mu}$$

But δ is a function of x, and

$$\frac{dm}{dx} = \frac{\rho^2 g \delta^2}{\mu} \cdot \frac{d\delta}{dx} \tag{10.2}$$

Next, the heat transfer, dQ, resulting from the condensation of an element of matter, dm, may be considered. This quantity of energy is conducted across the film to the wall, so by Fourier's law,

$$dQ = \frac{k \, dx(t_{sat.} - t_w)}{\delta} = \frac{k \, dx\theta_w}{\delta} \tag{10.3}$$

where dx is the area of the element of surface of unit depth. dQ may also be expressed as $dm h_{fg}$, assuming the vapour is saturated and there is no undercooling of liquid. From these relationships, dm may be expressed as

$$dm = \frac{k\theta_w dx}{h_{fg}\delta}$$

or

$$\frac{dm}{dx} = \frac{k\theta_w}{h_{fg}\delta} \tag{10.4}$$

Equations (10.2) and (10.4) may be combined to give

$$\frac{\rho^2 g \delta^2}{\mu} \frac{d\delta}{dx} = \frac{k\theta_w}{h_{fg}\delta}$$

This result may be integrated between the top of the surface down to x to give

$$\frac{\rho^2 g \delta^4}{4\mu} = \frac{k\theta_w x}{h_{fg}}$$

or

$$\delta = \left(\frac{4\mu k\theta_w x}{h_{fg}\rho^2 g}\right)^{\frac{1}{4}} \tag{10.5}$$

This is the relationship between film thickness and distance x from the top of the surface. From equation (10.3) a convection coefficient may be obtained as

$$h_x = \frac{dQ}{dx\theta_w} = \frac{k}{\delta}$$

and hence

$$Nu_x = \frac{h_x x}{k} = \frac{x}{\delta} = \left(\frac{h_{fg}\rho^2 g x^3}{4\mu k \theta_w}\right)^{\frac{1}{4}}$$

Thus the local Nusselt number may be written as

$$Nu_x = 0.706 \left(\frac{h_{fg}\rho^2 g x^3}{\mu k \theta_w}\right)^{\frac{1}{4}} \tag{10.6}$$

An average Nusselt number is then obtained by integrating h_x from 0 to x and dividing the result by the area $x \times$ unit depth, to give

$$\overline{Nu_x} = \frac{4}{3}Nu_x = 0.943 \left(\frac{h_{fg}\rho^2 g x^3}{\mu k \theta_w}\right)^{\frac{1}{4}} \tag{10.7}$$

The analysis on the horizontal tube of diameter d yields a similar expression for the average Nusselt number, thus

$$\overline{Nu_d} = 0.725 \left(\frac{h_{fg}\rho^2 g d^3}{\mu k \theta_w}\right)^{\frac{1}{4}} \tag{10.8}$$

EXAMPLE 10.1

Steam at $3.7\ \text{lbf/in}^2$ condenses on 1 in. diameter horizontal tubes which have a surface temperature of $130°F$. Calculate the average heat transfer coefficient.

Solution. The saturation temperature is $150°F$, at which $h_{fg} = 1008.2$ Btu/lb. The mean film temperature (at which liquid fluid properties are taken) is $140°F$. Hence, $\rho = 61.4\ \text{lb/ft}^3$, $\mu = 1.14\ \text{lb/ft h}$, and $k = 0.381\ \text{Btu/ft h deg F}$. $\theta_w = (t_{sat.} - t_w) = 20°F$.
    Equation (10.8) gives:

$$\overline{Nu_d} = 0.725 \left(\frac{1008.2 \times 61.4^2 \times 32.2 \times 60^4 \times 1^3}{1.14 \times 0.381 \times 20 \times 12^3}\right)^{\frac{1}{4}}$$

$$= 0.725 \times 570$$

$$= 413.0$$

$$\therefore \quad \bar{h} = 413 \times \frac{k}{d} = \frac{413 \times 0.381 \times 12}{1}$$

$$= 1890\ \text{Btu/ft}^2\ \text{h deg F}$$

Equation (10.7) for a vertical surface may be applied to a vertical tube provided the diameter is not small, when the liquid film becomes two-dimensional, and hence it is possible to compare the relative merits of horizontal and vertical tubes. Thus

$$\frac{\overline{Nu_d}}{\overline{Nu_x}} = \frac{0.725}{0.943}\left(\frac{d^3}{x^3}\right)^{\frac{1}{4}} = \frac{h_d d}{h_x x}$$

$$\therefore \quad \frac{h_d}{h_x} = 0.770\left(\frac{x}{d}\right)^{\frac{1}{4}}$$

If (x/d) is 75, say, it follows that $h_d = 2.26\,h_x$. Thus over twice the fluid is condensed with the tubes arranged horizontally, h_x being the coefficient for the vertical tube.

For more advanced topics on condensation the reader is referred to the literature. It is not possible to consider in this introductory text the effects of turbulence in the liquid film,[3] velocity of the condensing vapour,[4] superheat,[3] or condensing flow inside tubes.[5]

10.3. Boiling Heat Transfer

Heat transfer to boiling liquids is a subject at present under intensive study. It is of paramount importance in the power generation industry. Several fairly well defined regimes of heat transfer are now recognized, and values of heat transfer coefficient associated with each have been measured.

A simple experiment involving an electrically heated wire immersed in water illustrates the simpler boiling mechanisms.[6] The variation of heat flux with the difference in temperature between the wire and liquid has been observed by numerous investigators and the general form of the result is shown in Fig. 10.2. As the wire warms up initially heat transfer is by natural convection. As the wire temperature reaches a few degrees in excess of the saturation temperature streams of tiny bubbles will be observed to leave the surface of the wire. These bubbles are produced at nucleation sites, since a minor roughness of the surface is necessary for the bubble to form. Higher temperatures are found to be necessary for nucleation to begin if the surface is made especially smooth. Part 1–2 of the curve in Fig. 10.2 is natural convection, and this becomes steeper in region 2–3 as boiling proceeds. This initial boiling is known as nucleate boiling. The heat transfer rate is significantly

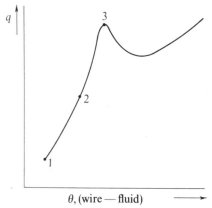

Fig. 10.2. The boiling curve, after Farber and Scorah (6).

improved by the stirring action of the bubbles. Bubble formation becomes increasingly energetic as point 3 is approached. At this point the bubbles tend to merge together to form a continuous vapour enclosure round the wire. When this happens nucleate boiling gives way to film boiling and there is a reduction in heat flux due to the thermally insulating effect of the vapour. This situation leads to a rapid increase in wire temperature and possible melting, unless the current input is quickly reduced. Once film boiling is safely established, the heat flux will again increase with temperature until the wire melts, the mechanism here being convection and radiation through the vapour.

Boiling processes may be further sub-divided when considering the flow of fluid vertically in a tube. The process may be associated with the type of flow.[7] Various flow regimes are shown in Fig. 10.3. These are: sub-cooled liquid flow, 'frothy' or 'bubbly' flow at low dryness fraction, 'churn' or 'slug' flow in which slugs of vapour appear, annular or climbing film flow, fog or dispersed liquid flow, and finally dry wall flow at the saturated steam condition. Associated boiling·processes are tabulated in Fig. 10.3. Sub-cooled nucleate and film boiling are examples of local boiling. There is no overall production of vapour; this is condensed in the main bulk of the fluid after being produced at the wall of the tube. Very high convection coefficients result because of the activity at the wall, and this heat transfer mechanism is finding application in other situations where a high convection coefficient is valuable. Saturated

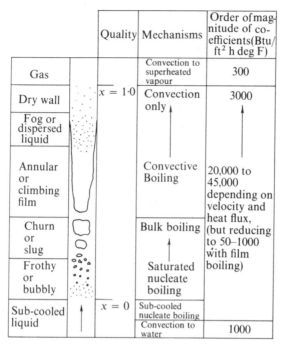

	Quality	Mechanisms	Order of magnitude of coefficients(Btu/ft^2 h deg F)
Gas		Convection to superheated vapour	300
Dry wall	$x = 1{\cdot}0$	Convection only	3000
Fog or dispersed liquid			
Annular or climbing film		Convective Boiling	20,000 to 45,000 depending on velocity and heat flux, (but reducing to 50–1000 with film boiling)
Churn or slug		Bulk boiling	
Frothy or bubbly		Saturated nucleate boiling	
Sub-cooled liquid	$x = 0$	Sub-cooled nucleate boiling	
		Convection to water	1000

Fig. 10.3. Flow and boiling regimes in a vertical heated tube. From data of Firman, Gardner, and Clapp (7). By courtesy of the Institution of Mechanical Engineers.

nucleate boiling occurs when the bulk fluid temperature has reached the saturation value, and is therefore associated with flow at low dryness fraction. This mechanism persists into the slug flow regime when it is termed bulk boiling. When, with the increasing velocities, annular flow is established, convective heat transfer between the annulus of liquid and the core of vapour takes place and the nucleate process tends to be suppressed. This is known as convective boiling. Initially, the vapour core is thought to be fairly dry, but with accelerated flow the liquid annulus is entrained as a dispersed spray or fog in the core. Once the liquid phase has left the tube wall, as in the dry wall region, the heat transfer coefficient drops rapidly. The mechanism is by convection and by conduction to individual droplets impinging on the wall. Finally, when the steam becomes superheated, heat transfer is by convection only. Film boiling is avoided in the foregoing as far as possible. It occurs with excessive heat fluxes and results in drastic reductions in the boiling coefficient and very high metal temperatures. The order of magnitude of the heat transfer coefficients associated with the type of flow and mechanism of heat transfer are also shown in Fig. 10.3. It will be observed that the coefficients vary over a considerable range.

It will be appreciated from what has been said so far that boiling heat transfer is a complex subject and to take the subject any further is beyond the scope of this text. Working formulae and procedures exist in the literature for the determination of boiling coefficients for design purposes, and the reader may refer to Bagley[8] for a recent statement from the boiler industry, and to Jakob[9] and to Hsu[3] for more comprehensive treatments of the subject.

PROBLEMS

To solve Questions 1 and 2 see also chapter 13.

1. An air heater consists of horizontal tubes 1 in. o.d. and $\frac{3}{4}$ in. i.d. arranged in vertical banks of twenty. Air passes inside the tubes and is heated from 90 to 290°F by saturated steam at 350°F which passes over the tubes. The mean air velocity is 75 ft/s and the air flow is 20,000 lb/h. Calculate the number and length of tubes required.

The heat transfer coefficient for saturated steam to tube surface (h_{sv}) can be found from

$$h_{sv} = 0.725 \left(\frac{k_c^3 \rho_c^2 g h_{fg}}{N d \mu_c \Delta t} \right)^{\frac{1}{4}} \text{ Btu/ft}^2 \text{ h deg F}$$

where the suffix c denotes condensate properties evaluated at the saturation temperature, g is the gravitational acceleration in ft/h², N is the number of horizontal tubes in a vertical bank, d is the tube o.d. in ft, Δt is the temperature difference between the saturated vapour and the tube surface and may be assumed to be 20°F. The other symbols have their usual meaning. (Ans. 396 tubes, 5.70 ft.) (University of Glasgow).

2. A vertical tubular condenser is specified as follows: Construction: Single pass, 200 tubes 1 in. o.d., $\frac{3}{4}$ in. i.d., 12 ft long.

Tube side: Water, tube velocity $v = 1.0$ ft/s, inlet 70°F, outlet 90°F. Film coefficient $h_w = 150(1 + 0.011t)v^{0.8}/d^{0.2}$ Btu/h ft² deg F where t = average water temperature deg F, d = tube i.d., inches.

Shell side: Condensing load $G' = 10,000$ lb/h vapour at 195°F to liquid at 195°F, latent heat $\lambda = 285$ Btu/lb, density $\rho = 50$ lb/ft³, conductivity $k = 0.10$ Btu/h ft deg F, viscosity $\mu = 1.5$ f.p.h. units. Film coefficient $h_c = 0.95(k^3 \rho^2 g N \pi D / \mu G')^{\frac{1}{3}}$ Btu/h ft² deg F where g = gravitational acceleration f/h², N = number of tubes, D = tube o.d., ft.

(i) From the duty calculate the overall heat transfer coefficient based on the outside area.

(ii) From the data, predict the value of this coefficient (assume negligible wall resistance).

(iii) Comment briefly on the two values obtained. (Ans. (i) 39·5 Btu/ft² h deg F, (ii) 88·5 Btu/ft² h deg F.) (*University of Leeds*).

3. Describe the 'Farber–Scorah Boiling Curve' together with the mechanism of heat transfer relating to each section of the curve. Discuss the following topics in relation to the heat transfer to a fluid in which nucleate boiling occurs:

(a) Temperature distribution in the fluid;
(b) The nature of the heating surface;
(c) The operating pressure.

(*University of Leeds*).

4. Steam is being condensed on flat vertical surfaces. If the drag on the steam side of the condensate film can be neglected, derive an expression for the local and mean heat transfer coefficient on the surface.

Discuss the assumptions which you make in the derivation.

If the surfaces are parallel and steam enters the space between two surfaces at the top, show how you would correct the derivation for the drag of the flowing steam on the condensate film. (*University of Leeds*).

5. Outline the Nusselt theory of film condensation, indicating the steps which lead to the following formula for the average surface heat transfer coefficient h_m during the condensation of a saturated vapour on a plane vertical surface:

$$Nu_m = \frac{h_m L}{K} = 0.943 \left(\frac{\rho^2 g L^3 h_{fg}}{\mu K \Delta T} \right)^{\frac{1}{4}}$$

L is the height of the surface, g the acceleration due to gravity, h_{fg} the enthalpy of evaporation, ΔT the difference between the temperatures of the vapour and the surface and ρ, μ, and K are respectively the density, absolute viscosity, and thermal conductivity of the condensate at the saturation temperature.

Saturated steam at 149°C is to be condensed in a cylinder of diameter 1·217 m and length 0·305 m, having its axis vertical. The curved wall is maintained at 10°C by external coolant and no condensation takes place on the two horizontal surfaces. The steam is fed in through a pipe in the top surface of the cylinder.

Determine the initial average surface heat transfer coefficient, and estimate the time taken to fill the container with water which may be assumed to remain at 149°C. (Ans. 4850 J/m² s deg C, 0·976 h.) (*University of Cambridge*).

REFERENCES

1. Nusselt, W. *Z. d. Ver. deutsch. Ing.*, Vol. 60, 541 (1916).
2. Nusselt, W. *Z. d. Ver. deutsch. Ing.*, Vol. 60, 569 (1916).
3. Hsu, S. T. *Engineering Heat Transfer*, D. Van Nostrand Company, Inc., Princeton (1963).
4. Carpenter, F. G., and Colburn, A. P. 'General Discussion on Heat Transfer', *I.Mech.E.London* (1951).

5. Akers, W. W., Deans, H. A., and Crosser, O. K. *Chem. Eng. Progr.*, Symposium Series, Vol. 55, No. 29, 171 (1959).
6. Farber, E. A., and Scorah, R. L. *Trans. ASME.*, Vol. 70, 369 (1948).
7. Firman, E. C., Gardner, G. C., and Clapp, R. M. *I.Mech.E. Symposium on Boiling Heat Transfer*, Manchester, Review Paper 1 (1965).
8. Bagley, R. *I.Mech.E. Symposium on Boiling Heat Transfer*, Manchester, Paper 13 (1965).
9. Jakob, M. *Heat Transfer*, Vol. 2, John Wiley, New York (1957).

11

Mass transfer by convection

The most firmly established theory of mass transfer is in the chemical engineering literature, where, it would seem, present thought has not changed significantly since the 1930's. In contrast, rapid advances in new technologies have led to the parallel growth of new theory for specific purposes, as in jet and rocket propulsion. Recently, Spalding[1] has embarked on the task of unifying mass transfer theory, to provide the same procedures in all applications. His work is based on the hypothetical model of mass movement at an interface known as Reynolds Flow. This model is based on the original ideas of Reynolds[2] concerning the processes of diffusion, shear and heat transfer at a phase interface. In contrast, chemical engineering literature on mass transfer is built around Stefan's law of diffusion.[3] The present chapter follows these traditional lines, since the scope is necessarily very limited. The student who wishes to follow mass transfer theory further than this limited introduction is well advised to follow Spalding's approach.

11.1. Processes of Diffusion

Two types of diffusion process in fluids are recognized. They are known as molecular and eddy diffusion. Individually they have similarities with the heat transfer processes of conduction and turbulent convection.

11.1.1. Molecular Diffusion. Molecular diffusion may be described by an Ohm's law type of equation, known as Fick's law, of the form

$$g_i = -D\frac{dc_i}{dy} \tag{11.1}$$

g_i is the mass transfer by diffusion of component i in moles per unit area and time, in the direction of the concentration gradient dc_i/dy. D is the molecular diffusion coefficient. As in conduction (the similarity with Fourier's law being noted), the positive flux is in a direction of negative gradient of the driving force. This equation may be applied to the diffusion of either liquids or gases, with the concentration c_i measured in moles per unit volume, but for gases it is more useful to express c_i as $p_i/R_m T$ where p_i is the partial pressure of i. Thus for gases equation (11.1) becomes

$$g_i = -\frac{D}{R_m T}\frac{dp_i}{dy} \tag{11.2}$$

Molecular diffusion is of primary importance in stagnant films. It also occurs across the direction of flow in moving fluids, if flow is laminar.

To consider a general steady state process of diffusion, a gas i is assumed to be diffusing through a second gas j at rest. A typical example would be the evaporation of water, i, into stagnant air, j, see Fig. 11.1. Mass transfer is only in the vertical direction, and diffusion of vapour upwards is controlled by equation (11.2). Since only two components are present, i and j, the total pressure P is the sum of the partial pressures p_i and p_j. Hence,

$$p_j = P - p_i$$

and

$$\frac{dp_j}{dy} = -\frac{dp_i}{dy}$$

A pressure gradient of opposite sign for j implies diffusion of j in the opposite direction to the diffusion of i. But there can be no actual transfer of j through the horizontal boundary surface (apart from a solution of j in i which is neglected), even though a diffusion of j relative to i exists. This situation results in a convective flow of i upwards, as well as the diffusion. If g_i is now the total mass transfer of i upwards, per unit area and time, then

$$g_i = -\frac{D}{R_m T}\frac{dp_i}{dy} + v_y\frac{p_i}{R_m T}$$

The convective flow is the product of velocity and concentration. v_y may be determined by writing a similar equation for component

j, with $g_j = 0$. Thus:

$$g_j = -\frac{D}{R_m T}\frac{dp_j}{dy} + v_y\frac{p_j}{R_m T} = 0$$

or, putting in terms of p_i,

$$g_j = \frac{D}{R_m T}\frac{dp_i}{dy} + v_y\frac{(P - p_i)}{R_m T} = 0$$

$$\therefore \quad v_y = -\frac{D}{(P - p_i)}\frac{dp_i}{dy}$$

Hence g_i is now given by:

$$g_i = -\frac{D}{R_m T}\frac{dp_i}{dy} - \frac{D}{(P - p_i)}\frac{p_i}{R_m T}\frac{dp_i}{dy}$$

$$= -\frac{D}{R_m T}\frac{P}{(P - p_i)}\frac{dp_i}{dy} \tag{11.3}$$

This equation is known as Stefan's law.[3]

With only two components involved, equation (11.3) may be expressed as

$$g_i = \frac{DP}{R_m T p_j}\frac{dp_j}{dy} \tag{11.4}$$

This is integrated between planes 1 and 2, Fig. 11.1, to give

$$g_i = \frac{DP}{R_m T(y_2 - y_1)}\ln\frac{p_{j2}}{p_{j1}} \tag{11.5}$$

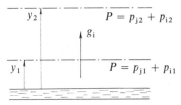

Fig. 11.1.   Vertical diffusion of evaporating fluid i into stagnant gas j.

where p_{j2} and p_{j1} are the partial pressures of the stagnant gas at planes 2 and 1. If a logarithmic mean pressure is introduced, such that

$$(p_j)_{lm} = \frac{p_{j2} - p_{j1}}{\ln p_{j2}/p_{j1}} \tag{11.6}$$

and if $\ln p_{j2}/p_{j1}$ is eliminated from equation (11.5), then

$$g_i = \frac{DP(p_{j2} - p_{j1})}{R_m T(p_j)_{lm}(y_2 - y_1)} \qquad (11.7)$$

With reference to Fig. 11.2 it can be seen that $p_{j2} = P - p_{i2}$ and

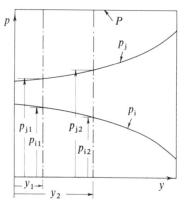

Fig. 11.2. Variation of partial pressures of diffusing vapour i into stagnant gas j.

$p_{j1} = P - p_{i1}$, and on substitution into equation (11.7) gives

$$g_i = \frac{DP(p_{i1} - p_{i2})}{R_m T(p_j)_{lm}(y_2 - y_1)} \qquad (11.8)$$

Just as in heat transfer where the process of convection can be described by the Newton equation, $q = h(t_1 - t_2)$, in which h is the convection coefficient, it is possible to describe mass transfer processes by a similar relationship

$$g_i = h_m(c_{i1} - c_{i2})$$

or for gases,

$$g_i = \frac{h_m}{R_m T}(p_{i1} - p_{i2}) \qquad (11.9)$$

h_m is the mass transfer or film coefficient, and the concentration or partial pressure difference is the mass transfer driving force.

Comparing equations (11.8) and (11.9) it is evident that

$$h_m = \frac{DP}{(p_j)_{lm}(y_2 - y_1)} \qquad (11.10)$$

Here $(y_2 - y_1)$ is the length or thickness of the material layer across which mass transfer is taking place.

11.1.2. Eddy Diffusion. Equation (11.1) for molecular diffusion may be extended to describe the turbulent condition, in a similar form to equations (7.3) and (7.12) for turbulent shear and heat transfer. Thus:

$$g_i = (D + \varepsilon_m)\frac{dc_i}{dy} \qquad (11.11)$$

This equation indicates that molecular diffusion is still present and that the contributions due to molecular and eddy diffusion are additive. ε_m is the eddy mass diffusivity for component i and is a measure of the mass transfer of i due to the action of turbulence. It must not be confused with ε, which is a measure of the transfer of momentum involving the entire mass of turbulent eddies.

11.2. Mass Transfer in Laminar and Turbulent Convection

In convective mass transfer, the existence of a boundary layer in which the concentration gradient of the diffusing medium varies between the wall value and the free stream value, may be assumed. The boundary layer will be all laminar, or turbulent with a laminar sublayer, depending on the free stream flow. When heat transfer by convection was introduced in chapter 6, the equations of momentum (6.5), and energy (6.7), when applied to a laminar boundary layer on a flat plate, were quoted. A similar equation of mass diffusion may be obtained, which is derived by consideration of the diffusion and convection of mass into a fluid element. Applied to a laminar boundary layer on a flat plate the equation is:

$$v_x\frac{\partial c_i}{\partial x} + v_y\frac{\partial c_i}{\partial y} = D\frac{\partial^2 c_i}{\partial y^2} \qquad (11.12)$$

A striking similarity between this equation and equations (6.5) and (6.7) is apparent. However, it should be noted that when momentum, energy, and mass transfer are occurring simultaneously in a laminar boundary layer, equations (6.5), (6.7), and (11.12) considered together represent a simplification of the true picture. This is because mass diffusion depends on temperature gradients as well as concentration gradients. The effect is very small except when the temperature gradients are very large, and consequently it is neglected.

When the boundary conditions of the above equations are considered for the case of heat and mass transfer in convective flow, an important difference will be found compared with the boundary conditions of convection heat transfer alone.

Thus in heat and mass transfer:

$$\text{At } y = 0, v_x = 0, v_y = v_w, c_i = c_{iw}, \theta = 0$$
$$\text{At } y = \text{free stream}, v_x = v_s, c_i = c_{is}, \theta = \theta_s$$

In heat transfer alone:

$$\text{At } y = 0, v_x = 0, v_y = 0, \theta = 0$$

$$\text{At } y = \text{free stream}, v_x = v_s, \theta = \theta_s$$

The difference is that v_y is not zero at the wall when mass transfer is taking place. If it can be assumed that v_w is zero then the energy and momentum equations have the same boundary conditions in the presence of mass transfer. In other words, the flow pattern and the heat transfer are not influenced by the existence of mass transfer. Whether or not v_w is small enough to be neglected will depend on the magnitude of the mass transfer taking place. *When the mass transfer of water vapour in air is being considered, which is the primary interest and scope of this treatment, then v_w may be neglected.* This is due to the very low concentrations of water vapour in air that are encountered, which makes the velocity v_w very small compared with other velocities of the flow field. This is an important simplification because it makes it possible to solve mass transfer problems by considering the similarity with heat transfer.

Consequently, it is not necessary to consider the boundary layer equations of heat and mass transfer any further, except to note the similarity of form between them. In considering heat transfer, it was pointed out that equations (6.5) and (6.7) lead to identical velocity and non-dimensionalized temperature profiles when $v = \alpha$, or when $Pr = 1$. Similarly, the velocity and non-dimensionalized concentration profiles are identical when $v = D$. v/D, the Schmidt number Sc, is equivalent to the Prandtl number in heat transfer.

The similarities between heat and mass transfer noted so far would lead one to expect that the mass transfer coefficient as defined by equation (11.9) would depend on dimensionless groups, in the same way that the heat transfer coefficient in convection can be expressed as a function of the Reynolds and Prandtl numbers. Thus it is found that

$$\frac{h_m l}{D} = f(Re_l Sc) \tag{11.13}$$

where $h_m l/D$ is the mass transfer Nusselt number, and is known as the Sherwood number Sh. This form of the Sherwood number may be used for fluids where concentrations are expressed in mole units. For gases, equation (11.10) indicates that a more appropriate dimensionless group is

$$\frac{h_m (p_j)_{lm}(y_2 - y_1)}{DP} = \frac{h_m l}{D} \frac{(p_j)_{lm}}{P} \tag{11.14}$$

$(y_2 - y_1)$ in equation (11.10) becomes the characteristic length l. It is to be noted that the factor $(p_j)_{lm}/P$ in equation (11.14) arises from consideration of the convective velocity normal to the wall, which was assumed above to be small enough to be neglected. If v_y in the analysis leading to equation (11.8) is neglected, then $(p_j)_{lm}/P$ would disappear. Thus, in consideration of simultaneous heat and mass transfer involving the air–water vapour system, the Sherwood number is $h_m l/D$. But for mass transfer in general, in the absence of heat transfer, the Sherwood number is $(h_m l/D)(p_j)_{lm}/P$.

Experimental studies of mass transfer in geometrical arrangements of practical importance have been made. In many cases, experiments have involved the evaporation of liquids, and particularly water, into air. A typical example is the evaporation of a liquid from an annular film inside a pipe to air flowing along the pipe. The work of Gilliland and Sherwood[4] includes data for water and various organic fluids of Schmidt number in the range 0·60–2·5, over a range of Reynolds number from 2000 to 35,000 and pressures between 0·1 and 3·0 atm. The Reynolds number is based on the velocity of the air relative to the pipe, not on the velocity of the air relative to the moving liquid film. The empirical relationship obtained is

$$\frac{h_m d}{D} \frac{(p_j)_{lm}}{P} = 0·023 Re_d^{0·83} Sc^{0·44} \tag{11.15}$$

The linear dimension is the pipe diameter d.

The similarity of equation (11.15) to the corresponding convective heat transfer equation is apparent. In general, if the dimensionless heat and mass transfer coefficients are compared for the special case of $D = \alpha$, then they are equal at a given Reynolds number. Thus,

$$\frac{h_m l}{D} = f(Re, Sc)$$

and

$$\frac{hl}{k} = f(Re, Pr)$$

But $D = \alpha$, so $Sc = v/D = v/\alpha = Pr$.

$$\therefore \quad \frac{h_m l}{D} = \frac{hl}{k}$$

$$\therefore \quad h_m = h\frac{D}{k} = h\frac{\alpha}{k} = \frac{h}{\rho c_p} \tag{11.16}$$

Thus h_m and h are simply related. This law was first derived by Lewis,[5] and is referred to as the Lewis relation. An alternative form is

$$h_m = \frac{h}{C_p} \tag{11.17}$$

where $C_p = \rho c_p$, and is a specific heat on a volume basis. By considering a turbulent mass and energy exchange, it can be shown that the Lewis relation is valid in turbulent flow even if D does not equal α. In laminar flow, the relation is valid only for $D = \alpha$. The group D/α is the Lewis number Le, and has the value of 1 in this special case.

11.3. Reynolds Analogy

The similarity between equations for heat transfer and momentum transfer led to the Reynolds analogy between heat transfer and fluid friction; in a similar manner an analogy may be deduced between mass transfer and fluid friction. The equations to be compared are, in laminar flow:

$$\tau = \rho v \frac{dv}{dy}, \quad \text{and} \quad g_i = D\frac{dc_i}{dy}$$

and in turbulent flow:

$$\tau = \rho(v + \varepsilon)\frac{dv}{dy}, \quad \text{and} \quad g_i = (D + \varepsilon_m)\frac{dc_i}{dy}$$

As in heat transfer, a simple analogy may be considered in which the flow is either all laminar, when ε and ε_m are zero, or the flow is all turbulent. It is also necessary to assume that g_i/τ is a constant across the depth of flow, which means that g_i and τ both vary in a similar manner with y. This implies similarity in the dimensionless contours of velocity and concentration across the flow, as when $Sc = 1$.

Considering laminar flow, the mass transfer equation integrated between the free or bulk stream s, and the wall w, is divided by the shear stress equation integrated between the same limits, to give:

$$\frac{g_{iw}}{\tau_w} = \frac{D(c_{is} - c_{iw})}{\rho v v_s} \tag{11.18}$$

This may be re-arranged to give the mass transfer coefficient, h_m. Thus:

$$h_m = \frac{g_{iw}}{c_{is} - c_{iw}} = \frac{\tau_w D}{\rho v v_s}$$

If the friction factor, $Cf = \tau_w/\frac{1}{2}\rho v_s^2$, is introduced, then

$$h_m = \frac{Cf}{2}\left(\frac{D}{v}\right)v_s \tag{11.19}$$

A mass transfer Stanton number may be assumed such that

$$(St)_M = \frac{(Sh)}{(Re) \times (Sc)}$$

$$\therefore \quad (St)_M = \frac{h_m l}{D} \cdot \frac{v}{v_s l} \cdot \frac{D}{v} = \frac{h_m}{v_s}$$

Hence, equation (11.19) may be written as

$$(St)_M = \frac{h_m}{v_s} = \frac{Cf}{2(Sc)} \tag{11.20}$$

The comparison with heat transfer is complete for the special case when $Sc = 1$.

In consideration of turbulent flow, the assumption that v and D are small in comparison with ε and ε_m may be made in addition to the assumption of similarity in velocity and concentration contour. The turbulent flow equations may be integrated and divided out to give:

$$\frac{g_{iw}}{\tau_w} = \frac{\varepsilon_m(c_{is} - c_{iw})}{\rho \varepsilon v_s} \tag{11.21}$$

This is re-arranged to give

$$h_m = \frac{g_{iw}}{c_{is} - c_{iw}} = \frac{\tau_w \varepsilon_m}{\rho \varepsilon v_s} = \frac{Cf}{2}\left(\frac{\varepsilon_m}{\varepsilon}\right) v_s$$

$$\therefore \quad (St)_M = \frac{Cf}{2(Sc)_\varepsilon} \tag{11.22}$$

where $(Sc)_\varepsilon$ is the turbulent Schmidt number $(\varepsilon/\varepsilon_m)$.

A more exact analysis will, of course, take into consideration the existence of a laminar sublayer which will be present at the solid boundary in the case of turbulent flow. Colburn[6] made a Prandtl–Taylor type analysis of Reynolds analogy for mass transfer for gases, and obtained the result:

$$h_m = \frac{\frac{1}{2}Cf \, v_s P/(p_j)_{lm}}{1 + v_b/v_s(Sc - 1)} \tag{11.23}$$

where v_b is the velocity at the limit of the laminar sublayer. By analogy with heat transfer, Chilton and Colburn[7] replaced the denominator of equation (11.23) by $Sc^{\frac{2}{3}}$. Since h_m/v_s is $(St)_M$, the above result then gives

$$(St)_M Sc^{\frac{2}{3}} \frac{(p_j)_{lm}}{P} = \frac{Cf}{2} = J_M \tag{11.24}$$

Thus, a mass transfer J-factor has the same value as the heat transfer J-factor, equation (7.27). Experimentally, it has been found that J and J_M have similar relationships with each other, though in cases where drag rather than pure friction exists, values are less than $\frac{1}{2}Cf$. For further information on this topic, the reader is referred to Sherwood and Pigford,[8] Chapter 3.

11.4. Combined Heat and Mass Transfer

In the treatment of simultaneous heat and mass transfer it is assumed that the presence of mass transfer does not affect the heat transfer equations. The approach is then by considerations of similarity.

11.4.1. The Wet and Dry Bulb Thermometer.

The combination of heat and mass transfer effects in many evaporative processes are the same as those in the wet and dry bulb thermometer.

The essential details of this instrument are shown in Fig. 11.3, and two simple equations may be written down to describe the simultaneous processes of heat and mass transfer. Thus:
Heat transfer:

$$h(t_a - t_f) = m_w h_{fg} \qquad (11.25)$$

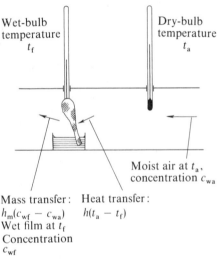

Wet-bulb temperature t_f

Dry-bulb temperature t_a

Moist air at t_a, concentration c_{wa}

Mass transfer: $h_m(c_{wf} - c_{wa})$ Wet film at t_f Concentration c_{wf}

Heat transfer: $h(t_a - t_f)$

Fig. 11.3.   *Details of the wet and dry bulb thermometer.*

m_w is the mass of water in lb or kg evaporating from unit area of the wet wick in unit time. h_{fg} is the enthalpy of evaporation at the wet wick temperature.
Mass transfer:

$$h_m(c_{wf} - c_{wa}) = g_w \qquad (11.26)$$

This follows from equation (11.9), and c_{wf} is the concentration of water vapour in air at the wet wick, and c_{wa} the concentration in the surrounding air. Normally, equation (11.26) is used with mole units, but for present purposes it is convenient to express the concentrations of water vapour in mass per unit volume, then g_w becomes equal to m_w in equation (11.25). The two equations are then combined to give

$$\frac{h(t_a - t_f)}{h_m(1/v_{wf} - 1/v_{wa})} = h_{fg} \qquad (11.27)$$

The concentrations now become the reciprocal of the specific volumes at the film and air conditions. Equations (7.27) and (11.24) may now be used to relate the heat and mass transfer coefficients. These two equations give

$$St\,Pr^{\frac{2}{3}} = \frac{Cf}{2} = (St)_M Sc^{\frac{2}{3}}\frac{(p_j)_{lm}}{P}$$

But the group $(p_j)_{lm}/P$ may be made equal to 1, and hence:

$$\frac{h}{h_m} = \rho c_p \left(\frac{Sc}{Pr}\right)^{\frac{2}{3}} \qquad (11.28)$$

This result is now substituted in equation (11.27), and also α/D may be substituted for Sc/Pr to give

$$\frac{\rho c_p}{h_{fg}} \left(\frac{\alpha}{D}\right)^{\frac{2}{3}} \times (t_a - t_f) = \frac{1}{v_{wf}} - \frac{1}{v_{wa}} \qquad (11.29)$$

EXAMPLE 11.1

An hygrometer gives a dry bulb temperature of 70°F and a wet bulb temperature of 60°F. Calculate the relative humidity of the air.

The Schmidt number of water vapour diffusing in air may be taken as 0·6 and the Prandtl number of air, 0·7, hence $\alpha/D = 0·856$, and $(\alpha/D)^{\frac{2}{3}} = 0·90$.

ρ is the density of air at the mean temperature, 65°F, and is 0·0756 lb/ft³. c_p is 0·24 Btu/lb deg F.

Solution. At the wet wick air is saturated with water vapour, and hence the partial pressure of the vapour from steam tables is 0·256 lbf/in². R_w for water vapour is $1545/18 = 85·8$.

$$\therefore \quad \frac{1}{v_{wf}} = \frac{p_w}{R_w T} = \frac{0.256 \times 144}{85.8 \times 520} = 0.000826 \text{ lb/ft}^3$$

h_{fg} at 60°F is 1060 Btu/lb.

Equation (11.29) is now used to find $1/v_{wa}$.

$$\frac{0.0756 \times 0.24}{1060}(0.90)(70 - 60) = 0.000826 - 1/v_{wa}$$

$$\therefore \quad 0.000153 = 0.000826 - 1/v_{wa}$$

and

$$1/v_{wa} = 0.000673$$

Working back from this result the partial pressure of vapour may be found.

$$p_w = \frac{0.000673 \times 85.8 \times 530}{144} = 0.212 \text{ lbf/in}^2$$

At 70°F, the saturation pressure is 0.363 lbf/in^2, hence the relative humidity is $0.212/0.363 = 58.5$ per cent. The same result is obtained by comparing the specific volume $1/0.000673$ with the saturation value at 70°F.

A less accurate solution to this problem would have been obtained by using the Lewis relation. The relation between the heat and mass transfer coefficients would be:

$$\frac{h}{h_m} = \rho c_p, \quad \text{instead of} \quad \frac{h}{h_m} = \rho c_p \left(\frac{\alpha}{D}\right)^{\frac{2}{3}}$$

In general, equation (11.28) is to be preferred, since even if flow is turbulent, the Lewis relation is invalidated (except when $Le = 1$) by the existence of the laminar sublayer. Equation (11.28) resulted from considerations of the existence of the sublayer.

PROBLEMS

1. Calculate the rate of evaporation from the surface of a pond of area 2000 m^2 into still air at 25°C. The relative humidity of the atmosphere 0.3 m above the surface of the pond may be assumed constant (due to air currents at that level) at 50 per cent. (Ans. 11.35 kg/h.)

2. Air at 25°C and of 40 per cent relative humidity enters a vertical 8 cm diameter pipe at 4 m/s. Water also at 25°C runs slowly down the inside surface of the pipe. Calculate the length of pipe necessary to saturate the air. (Ans. 4.74 m.)

3. Air at atmospheric pressure and 60°F having a relative humidity of 45 per cent flows at a velocity of 16 ft/s over a porous plate 1 ft long. Water is forced through the porous plate at a rate equal to the evaporation loss so that the exposed surface is always wet.

The plate is maintained at a temperature of 50°F by supplying heat to the plate. Use the following information to estimate the rate at which this heat should be supplied.

Kinematic viscosity 0·56 ft²/h; thermal diffusivity 0·79 ft²/h.
Diffusivity of water vapour in air, 0·85 ft²/h
Thermal conductivity, 0·014 Btu/ft h deg F
Latent heat of water, 1067 Btu/lb
Free stream concentration, $0·31 \times 10^{-3}$ lb/ft³
Interface concentration, $0·58 \times 10^{-3}$ lb/ft³.

The average Nusselt number over a distance x from the leading edge of a hot plate is

$$Nu = 0·66(Pr)^{\frac{1}{3}}(Re_x)^{\frac{1}{2}}$$

(Ans. 16·6 Btu/ft² h.) (*University of Leeds*).

4. On the assumption of the similarity between the processes of heat and mass transfer and the equality of the molecular diffusivities of heat and mass, derive the Lewis relation for mass transfer,

$$h_D = \frac{h}{s_p}$$

where h_D and h are the mass and heat transfer coefficients respectively and s_p is the volumetric specific heat at constant pressure of the gas carrying the transferred substance. Under what conditions does the relation apply regardless of the equality of the molecular diffusivities of heat and mass?

Moist air at 60°F, 14·7 psia and of relative humidity 20 per cent, blows over the surface of a square cooling pond of 50 ft side, containing water at 120°F. The mean velocity of the air is 20 ft/s and is parallel to one pair of sides. Assuming that the mean Nusselt number for heat transfer in longitudinal flow over a plane surface is given by

$$\overline{Nu}_x = 0·036\,Pr^{\frac{1}{3}}(Re_x^{0·8} - 23,100)$$

estimate the rate in lb per hour at which water is lost from the surface of the pond, (*a*) by using the Lewis relation, and (*b*) by any other method in which the assumption that $D = \alpha$ is not made. Comment on the answer.

The effect of the presence of water vapour on the transport properties of air may be neglected.

Kinematic viscosity of air, $v = 0·57$ ft²/h.
Thermal diffusivity of air, $\alpha = 0·77$ ft²/h.
Diffusion coefficient for water vapour in air, $D = 1·08$ ft²/h.

(Ans. (*a*) 2330 lb/h, (*b*) 1935 lb/h, using equation (11.28).) (*University of Cambridge*).

REFERENCES

1. Spalding, D. B. *Convective Mass Transfer*, Edward Arnold (Publishers) Ltd., London (1963).
2. Reynolds, O. *Proc. Manchester Lit. Phil. Soc.*, Vol. 8 (1874).
3. Stefan, J. *Sitz. Akad. Wiss. Wien*, Vol. 63, 63 (1871); Vol. 65, 323 (1872).
4. Gilliland, E. R., and Sherwood, T. K. *Ind. Eng. Chem.*, Vol. 26, 516 (1934).
5. Lewis, W. K. *Trans. Amer. Inst. Chem. Engrs*, Vol. 20, 9 (1927).
6. Colburn, A. P. *Ind. Eng. Chem.*, Vol. 22, 967 (1930).
7. Chilton, T. H., and Colburn, A. P. *Ind. Eng. Chem.*, Vol. 26, 1183 (1934).
8. Sherwood, T. K., and Pigford, R. L. *Absorption and Extraction*, McGraw-Hill Book Company, Inc., New York (1952).

Section 3
Combined Conduction and Convection Heat Transfer

12

Extended surfaces

Convection from a solid surface to a surrounding fluid is limited by the area of that surface. It would seem reasonable, therefore, that if the surface area could be extended, then a gain in total heat transfer would be achieved. This is done by adding fins to the surface. Heat transfer is then by conduction along the fin, and by convection from the surface of the fin. It is likely that the convection coefficient of the basic surface will be altered by the addition of fins, due to the new flow pattern involved and the fact that the temperature of the fin surface will not be uniform. Though the *average* surface temperature is reduced by the addition of fins, the total heat transfer is increased. In the treatment that follows it is assumed that the convection coefficient is known. The Nusselt numbers of finned surfaces may be determined experimentally.

There are various types of fin, the most common being the straight fin, the spine, and annular fin. The straight fin is rectangular in shape and generally of uniform cross-section, and the spine is simply a short thin rod protruding from the surface. Annular fins are often found if the primary or basic surface is cylindrical. Examples are to be found in heat exchangers and air-cooled petrol engines. Examples of annular fins for heat exchanger applications are shown in Fig. 12.1. Extended surface nuclear fuel cans are shown in Fig. 12.2. These are both straight and spiral in form.

Only the straight fin and spine will be considered here in detail. Fins of non-uniform cross-section and annular fins are more complex mathematically, and the reader is referred elsewhere for details.[1,2,3]

12.1. The Straight Fin and Spine

These are shown in Fig. 12.3. The straight fin has length L, and height l (from root to tip). These definitions are used whatever the

159

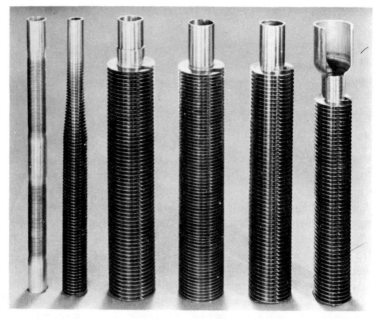

Fig. 12.1. Examples of 'Integron' extended surface tubing made for heat exchanger applications. Photograph by courtesy of Imperial Metal Industries (Kynoch) Limited.

actual orientation of the fin may be. In developing the theory of heat transfer in a fin it is assumed that the thickness, or diameter of the spine, is small compared with the length. Conduction along the fin may then be assumed to be one-dimensional. The conduction and convection heat transfers involved are shown in Fig. 12.4. Two important dimensions of fins are their area of cross-section A, and their perimeter P. In the straight fin it is convenient to assume that a is small compared with L. Thus:

$$\text{Straight fins} \quad A = La, \qquad P = 2L$$
$$\text{Spines} \qquad\quad A = \tfrac{1}{4}\pi d^2, \qquad P = \pi d$$

Consider an element of a fin or spine as shown in the figure. Conduction into the element at x is Q_x. This must be equal to the sum of the conduction out of the element at $x + \mathrm{d}x$ and the

Fig. 12.2. Examples of magnesium alloy fuel cans with extended surfaces for gas-cooled nuclear reactors. Photograph by courtesy of Imperial Metal Industries (Kynoch) Limited.

convection from the surface of the edge of the element. Thus

$$Q_x = -kA\frac{dt}{dx}$$

$$Q_{(x+dx)} = -kA\frac{dt}{dx} - kA\frac{d^2t}{dx^2}dx$$

$$Q_h = hP\,dx(t - t_s)$$

and

$$Q_x = Q_{(x+dx)} + Q_h$$

$$\therefore \quad -kA\frac{d^2t}{dx^2}dx + hP\,dx(t - t_s) = 0$$

$$\therefore \quad \frac{d^2t}{dx^2} - \frac{hP}{kA}(t - t_s) = 0$$

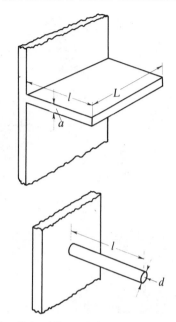

Fig. 12.3. The straight fin and the spine.

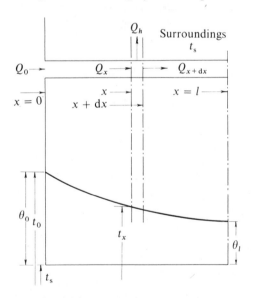

Fig. 12.4. Heat transfer from an extended surface.

Since t_s is assumed a constant surroundings temperature, $(t - t_s)$ may be replaced by θ, and d^2t/dx^2 becomes $d^2\theta/dx^2$.

$$\therefore \quad \frac{d^2\theta}{dx^2} - \frac{hP}{kA}\theta = 0$$

This differential equation in θ has a solution of the form:

$$\theta = C_1 e^{mx} + C_2 e^{-mx} \tag{12.1}$$

where

$$m = \left(\frac{hP}{kA}\right)^{\frac{1}{2}} \tag{12.2}$$

and C_1 and C_2 are constants of integration to be determined from boundary conditions.

The first boundary condition is that $\theta = \theta_0$ at $x = 0$. Therefore, from equation (12.1):

$$\theta_0 = C_1 + C_2 \tag{12.3}$$

The second boundary condition depends on the heat transfer from the tip of the fin. If the fin may be assumed long and thin this is very small and may be assumed to be zero with very little error.

$$\therefore \quad \left(\frac{d\theta}{dx}\right)_{x=l} = 0$$

$$\therefore \quad mC_1 e^{ml} - mC_2 e^{-ml} = 0 \tag{12.4}$$

Solution of equations (12.3) and (12.4) yields the values of C_1 and C_2, i.e.,

$$C_1 = \frac{\theta_0 e^{-ml}}{e^{ml} + e^{-ml}}, \quad \text{and} \quad C_2 = \frac{\theta_0 e^{ml}}{e^{ml} + e^{-ml}}$$

Substitution of these values back into equation (12.1) gives

$$\theta = \theta_0\left[\frac{e^{m(l-x)} + e^{-m(l-x)}}{e^{ml} + e^{-ml}}\right]$$

$$\therefore \quad \frac{\theta}{\theta_0} = \frac{\cosh m(l-x)}{\cosh ml} \tag{12.5}$$

Even though it was assumed that $(d\theta/dx)_{(x=l)} = 0$, the temperature at the end of the fin is still above t_s, and is given by

$$\theta_l = \frac{\theta_0}{\cosh ml} \qquad (12.6)$$

This is obtained by putting $x = l$ in equation (12.5).

The total heat transfer from the fin is obtained by considering the conduction into the fin at the root. Thus:

$$Q_0 = -kA\left(\frac{d\theta}{dx}\right)_{x=0}$$

$$= mkA\theta_0\left[\frac{\sinh m(l-x)}{\cosh ml}\right]_{x=0}$$

$$= mkA\theta_0 \tanh ml \qquad (12.7)$$

This result applies equally to the straight fin and spine, the appropriate value of m has merely to be substituted.

If the fin is comparatively short the assumption of no heat transfer from the tip of the fin is not valid. Under these conditions the heat transfer at the tip is given by

$$-kA\left(\frac{d\theta}{dx}\right)_{x=l} = +hA\theta_l$$

$$\therefore \quad -k(mC_1 e^{ml} - mC_2 e^{-ml}) = +h\theta_l \qquad (12.8)$$

The constants C_1 and C_2 may now be obtained by solving equations (12.3) and (12.8). Substituting for C_2 in (12.8) and eliminating θ_l by using (12.1):

$$-k[mC_1 e^{ml} - m(\theta_0 - C_1)e^{-ml}] = +h[C_1 e^{ml} + (\theta_0 - C_1)e^{-ml}]$$

This then gives:

$$C_1 = \frac{\theta_0[e^{-ml} - (h/km)e^{-ml}]}{(e^{ml} + e^{-ml}) + (h/km)(e^{ml} - e^{-ml})}$$

and

$$C_2 = \frac{\theta_0[e^{ml} + (h/km)e^{ml}]}{(e^{ml} + e^{-ml}) + (h/km)(e^{ml} - e^{-ml})}$$

and on substituting back into equation (12.1) gives

$$\frac{\theta}{\theta_0} = \frac{e^{m(l-x)} + e^{-m(l-x)} + (h/km)[e^{m(l-x)} - e^{-m(l-x)}]}{(e^{ml} + e^{-ml}) + (h/km)(e^{ml} - e^{-ml})}$$

which may be expressed as

$$\frac{\theta}{\theta_0} = \frac{\cosh m(l - x) + (h/km) \sinh m(l - x)}{\cosh ml + (h/km) \sinh ml} \tag{12.9}$$

The temperature difference at the end of the fin is given by

$$\theta_l = \frac{\theta_0}{\cosh ml + (h/km) \sinh ml} \tag{12.10}$$

The heat transfer from the fin is obtained as before by considering $(d\theta/dx)_{x=0}$. Thus

$$\begin{aligned}
Q_0 &= -kA\left(\frac{d\theta}{dx}\right)_{x=0} \\
&= -kA\theta_0 \left[\frac{-m \sinh m(l - x) - (h/k) \cosh m(l - x)}{\cosh ml + (h/km) \sinh ml}\right]_{x=0} \\
&= mkA\theta_0 \left[\frac{\sinh ml + (h/km) \cosh ml}{\cosh ml + (h/km) \sinh ml}\right] \\
&= mkA\theta_0 \left[\frac{\tanh ml + h/km}{1 + (h/km) \tanh ml}\right] \tag{12.11}
\end{aligned}$$

EXAMPLE 12.1

A metal tank containing cooling oil is to have its heat dissipation rate by convection increased by 70 per cent by the addition of fins to the wall surface. The fins will be 0·6 cm thick and spaced 0·1 m apart, between centres. The surface temperature of the tank is 95°C and the surrounding atmospheric temperature 15°C. The natural convection coefficient of the surface is 34 watt/m^2 deg C. Determine the height of each fin (i.e., distance between root and tip) on the assumption that the convection coefficient remains unchanged, that the surface temperature of the tank is expected to drop to 90°C when fins are fitted, and that heat transfer from the tips of the fins is neglected. k for the metal of fin and tank wall is 276 watt/m deg C.

Solution. Original heat transfer rate $= 34(95 - 15) = 2720 \text{ watt/m}^2$. Hence, the new rate is to be $1·7 \times 2720 = 4630 \text{ watt/m}^2$. 1 m^2 of primary surface is reduced to 0·94 m^2 by the addition of ten fins each 0·006 m thick. Heat transfer from this surface will be $34(90 - 15) \times 0·94 = 2400$ watt/m^2.

∴ 2230 watt must be dissipated by 10 fins each 1 m long.

∴ Each fin dissipates 223 watt/m length.

From equation (12.2)

$$m = \left(\frac{34 \times 2}{276 \times 0·006}\right)^{\frac{1}{2}} = 41^{\frac{1}{2}} = 6·4$$

This neglects the thickness of the fin in calculating the perimeter. Then, using equation (12.7),

$$Q_0 = mkA\theta_0 \tanh ml$$

$$= 6·4 \times 276 \times (1 \times 0·006) \times 75 \times \tanh(6·4 \times l)$$

∴ $223 = 794 \tanh(6·4\,l)$

∴ $0·282 = \tanh(6·4\,l)$

or

$$6·4\,l = 0·290$$

$$l = 0·0453 \text{ m}$$

$$= 4·53 \text{ cm}$$

12.2. Limit of Usefulness of the Straight Fin

It is important to recognize the fact that fins may not necessarily improve heat transfer from a surface, and the conditions under which fins will not be useful must be investigated before any design work is contemplated. There are only two possibilities to consider, either increasing a fin height will improve heat transfer, or in some circumstances reducing the fin height will give an improvement, and the limiting condition is that $dQ_0/dl = 0$.

The equation for heat transfer from a fin with the end condition given by (12.8) may be considered (equation (12.11)). In this equation, m, k, A, and θ_0 are constants, and therefore it is possible to write

$$\frac{\mathrm{d}}{\mathrm{d}l}\left[\frac{\tanh ml + h/mk}{1 + (h/mk)\tanh ml}\right] = 0$$

∴ $$\frac{\dfrac{[1 + (h/mk)\tanh ml]m}{\cosh^2 ml} - \dfrac{[\tanh ml + (h/mk)]h/k}{\cosh^2 ml}}{[1 + (h/mk)\tanh ml]^2} = 0$$

This will be zero when the numerator is zero, i.e., if

$$m[1 + (h/mk)\tanh ml] - (\tanh ml + h/mk)h/k = 0$$

$$\therefore \quad m - h^2/mk^2 = 0$$

$$\therefore \quad mk = h \qquad\qquad (12.12)$$

If this result is substituted back into equation (12.11), it is found that

$$Q_0 = hA\theta_0$$

which is the heat transfer from the surface occupied by the fin root, if the fin were not there. If $mk > h$, then Q_0 will be larger than this value, and the provision of fins will be worth-while. For the straight fin, equation (12.12) leads to the result that

$$\frac{2k}{hA} > 1 \qquad\qquad (12.13)$$

This, then, is the requirement which indicates that fins will improve the heat transfer from the surface.

12.3. Fin Effectiveness and Overall Coefficients

A fin effectiveness may be defined by relating the actual fin performance to that of an 'ideal fin' which has a uniform temperature all along its surface equal to the temperature at the root. Such a fin would result if constructed of a material having infinite thermal conductivity. The heat transfer from an ideal fin would be defined by

$$Q_0^* = Plh\theta_0 \qquad\qquad (12.14)$$

neglecting heat transfer from the end.

Taking the heat transfer from the actual fin to be given by (12.7)

$$Q_0 = mkA\theta_0 \tanh ml$$

then the fin effectiveness, η_f, would be given by

$$\eta_f = \frac{Q_0}{Q_0^*} = \frac{mkA\theta_0 \tanh ml}{Plh\theta_0}$$

This reduces to

$$\frac{Q_0}{Q_0^*} = \frac{A^{\frac{1}{2}}k^{\frac{1}{2}} \tanh ml}{h^{\frac{1}{2}}P^{\frac{1}{2}}l}$$

$$\therefore \quad \frac{Q_0}{Q_0^*} = \frac{\tanh ml}{ml} \qquad\qquad (12.15)$$

If the fin which has a significant end heat transfer is compared with the ideal fin as defined by (12.14) then

$$\eta_f = \frac{\tanh ml + h/km}{ml + (hl/k)\tanh ml} \qquad (12.16)$$

The fin effectiveness is a useful idea in relation to the next topic to be considered, the overall heat transfer coefficients of surfaces which have fins. In chapter 3, overall coefficients were derived for plane and cylindrical surfaces. Similar coefficients can be written for surfaces, both plane and cylindrical, on which fins have been added.

If A_s is the area of the total fin surface per unit area of primary or basic surface, then the total surface area will be $1 + A_s$. The basic surface, at θ_0 relative to the surroundings, is fully effective. The fin surface is not fully effective owing to the temperature drop along the fin length, but $\eta_f A_s$ is an area of surface which is fully effective, i.e., at θ_0 relative to the surroundings. It is then possible to compare the total of fully effective surface, $1 + \eta_f A_s$, to the total surface, $1 + A_s$, to obtain an equivalent effectiveness of the finned surface, η_{fe}. Thus

$$\eta_{fe} = \frac{1 + \eta_f A_s}{1 + A_s} \qquad (12.17)$$

A plane slab of conducting material finned on both surfaces is shown in Fig. 12.5. The temperatures of the primary surfaces are t_1 and t_2, and the thickness of the slab is x. Heat transfer by convection from fluid a to the a-fins (per unit area of slab) is given by

$$Q = -h_a[\eta_{fe}(1 + A_s)]_a(t_1 - t_a)$$

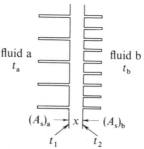

fluid a
t_a

fluid b
t_b

$(A_s)_a$ $\rightarrow$ x $\leftarrow$ $(A_s)_b$

t_1 t_2

Fig. 12.5.   Plane finned surfaces separating two fluids.

Similarly, from the b-fins to fluid b

$$Q = -h_b[\eta_{fe}(1 + A_s)]_b(t_b - t_2)$$

The heat transfer by conduction across the slab is

$$Q = -\frac{k}{x}(t_2 - t_1)$$

These three quantities are, of course, equal. The three equations may be combined to give

$$Q = -U(t_b - t_a)$$

where U is the overall heat transfer coefficient and is given by

$$U = 1 \bigg/ \left\{ \frac{1}{h_a[\eta_{fe}(1 + A_s)]_a} + \frac{x}{k} + \frac{1}{h_b[\eta_{fe}(1 + A_s)]_b} \right\} \quad (12.18)$$

In this analysis, the group $[\eta_{fe}(1 + A_s)]_a$ means the values of η_{fe} and A_s are taken for the a-fins, and similarly for the b-fins.

A similar result may be obtained for a tube finned internally and externally, as shown in Fig. 12.6. Unit length of tube may be considered and the following three equations for heat transfer may be written:

Convection inside: $\quad Q = -h_a 2\pi r_1[\eta_{fe}(1 + A_s)]_a(t_1 - t_a)$

Conduction: $\quad Q = -\dfrac{2\pi k}{\ln r_2/r_1}(t_2 - t_1)$

Convection outside: $\quad Q = -h_b 2\pi r_2[\eta_{fe}(1 + A_s)]_b(t_b - t_2)$

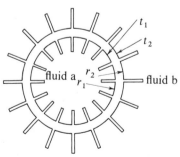

Fig. 12.6. *Cylindrical finned surfaces separating two fluids.*

These equations then lead to the result

$$Q = -U_L(t_b - t_a),$$

where

$$U_L = 1 \bigg/ \left\{ \frac{1}{2\pi r_1[\eta_{fe}(1 + A_s)]_a h_a} + \frac{\ln r_2/r_1}{2\pi k} \right.$$

$$\left. + \frac{1}{2\pi r_2[\eta_{fe}(1 + A_s)]_b h_b} \right\} \qquad (12.19)$$

This has units of watt/m deg C, or the equivalent. It is to be noted in this analysis that $\eta_{fe}(1 + A_s)$ is fully effective surface area per unit area of primary surface. This must then be multiplied by the area of primary surface per unit length, $2\pi r$. For the unfinned surface this reduces to

$$U_L = 1 \bigg/ \left(\frac{1}{2\pi r_1 h_a} + \frac{\ln r_2/r_1}{2\pi k} + \frac{1}{2\pi r_2 h_b} \right) \qquad (12.20)$$

Suffix L denotes U for unit length of tube.

Alternative expressions for U in terms of unit area of tube surface may also be obtained. If U_L in equation (12.19) is divided by $2\pi r_2$, the area of external primary surface per unit length, the result is

$$U_A = 1 \bigg/ \left\{ \frac{r_2}{r_1[\eta_{fe}(1 + A_s)]_a h_a} + \frac{r_2 \ln r_2/r_1}{k} \right.$$

$$\left. + \frac{1}{[\eta_{fe}(1 + A_s)]_b h_b} \right\} \qquad (12.21)$$

This has units of watt/m^2 (external primary surface) deg C, or the equivalent. The corresponding result for the unfinned surface is

$$U_A = 1 \bigg/ \left(\frac{r_2}{r_1 h_a} + \frac{r_2 \ln r_2/r_1}{k} + \frac{1}{h_b} \right) \qquad (12.22)$$

This is again in terms of external tube surface area.

These results are used in heat exchanger theory, in chapter 13.

PROBLEMS

1. Show that the rate of heat transmission through a fin of constant section extending from a wall at temperature θ_w into a fluid at temperature θ_f, heat transfer from the end of the fin being neglected, is given by

$$q = \sqrt{(hPkA)}(\theta_w - \theta_f) \tanh \left(\sqrt{\frac{hP}{kA}} \cdot l \right)$$

where h is the surface heat transfer coefficient, k is the thermal conductivity of the fin material, P and A are the perimeter and cross-sectional area respectively of the fin. Calculate the rate of heat transfer per square foot of wall area from water at 140°F to air at 60°F through a plane wall 0·5 in. thick having a smooth surface on the water side and fins extending into the air. The fins are of circular section, 0·25 in. diameter and 4 in. long at 1·5 in. square pitch. Both the fins and the wall are of steel having a thermal conductivity of 26 Btu/h ft deg F. The surface heat transfer coefficient on the water side is 4 Btu/h ft² deg F and that on the air side is 2 Btu/h ft² deg F. What is the overall heat transfer efficiency of the finned surface? (Ans.: 143 Btu/h, 67 per cent). (*University College, London*).

2. A long bar, having a perimeter P and cross-sectional area A, is heated at one end and loses heat freely to the atmosphere from the surface and the other end. If the loss of heat from the surface is proportional to the temperature difference between the surface and the air, show that the temperature distribution along the bar is in accordance with the differential equation

$$\frac{d^2\theta}{dx^2} = \frac{\sigma}{k}\frac{d\theta}{dt} + \frac{PS}{Ak}\theta$$

where σ and k are the specific heat, per unit volume, and the thermal conductivity, respectively, for the material of the bar and S is the surface heat transfer coefficient. Hence show that, for the bar under consideration and under steady conditions, the temperature θ_x at any point distance x from the heated end of the bar is given by

$$\theta_x = \frac{\theta_0}{1 + Ge^{-2ml}}\left(e^{-mx} + Ge^{-2ml}e^{mx}\right)$$

where

$$G = \frac{km - S}{km + S} \quad \text{and} \quad m = \left(\frac{PS}{Ak}\right)^{\frac{1}{2}}$$

In order to measure the temperature of heated air flowing along a pipe, a thermometer pocket, of the form shown in the figure, is screwed into the wall of the pipe and projects into the air stream.

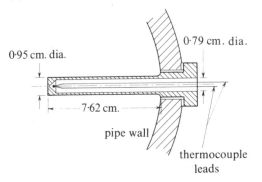

0·95 cm. dia.

0·79 cm. dia.

7·62 cm.

pipe wall

thermocouple leads

The temperature of the wall of the duct is 93·4°C and the thermocouple reads 182°C but, owing to conduction along the walls of the thermometer pocket, the thermocouple indicates a temperature below the true air temperature.

Estimate the true temperature of the air.

The heat transferred from the gas stream to a cylinder placed at right angles to the direction of flow is given by

$$Nu = 0·2\ Re^{0·6}$$

For the air in the duct the following properties may be assumed:

$$k = 0·0367, \quad \mu = 0·26 \times 10^{-4}, \quad \rho = 0·77$$

all in J, m, s, deg C units and for the material of the thermometer pocket $k = 121$ in the same units. The air velocity is 15·2 m/s. (Ans.: 195°C.) (*King's College, London*).

3. A bar simulating a gas turbine blade, cooled at the root, is 10·2 cm long and has a cross-sectional area (A) 1·93 cm^2, and a perimeter (p) of 7·6 cm. Gas at 815°C streams across it, and one end is cooled to 483°C. The mean heat transfer coefficient for the gas flow conditions can be assumed constant over the surface at 284 J/m^2 s deg C, and the thermal conductivity of the material of the bar (k) is 26 J/m s deg C. Show that

$$\frac{\theta_x}{\theta_r} = \frac{\cosh mL(1 - x/L)}{\cosh mL}$$

where

$$\theta_x = t_g - t_x, \quad \theta_r = t_g - t_r, \quad m = \sqrt{\frac{hp}{kA}}$$

L is the length of the bar and x the distance from the cooled end, t_g being the gas temperature and t_x and t_r the appropriate blade temperatures. Hence find the heat passing to the cooled end of the bar in J/s. Neglect the heat lost from the uncooled end of the bar. (Ans.: 110 J/s.) (*Queen Mary College, London*).

4. Heat flows from a body A along a wire of diameter d and length l, the other end of the wire being connected to a body B. The conductivity of the wire is k and the surface coefficient of heat transfer $\frac{1}{4}\alpha^2 kd$.

The temperature of the body A is maintained at θ_A above the temperature of the environment, and the temperature of the body B is θ_B above the temperature of the environment. Derive an expression for the temperature of the wire at x from A, and deduce the particular values of θ_B for which

(a) heat flow into B is one-half of the heat flow from A,

(b) heat flow into B is zero. (*University of Oxford*).

5. A wire, cross-sectional area A, perimeter p, and length l, has one section maintained at a steady temperature t_0 above that of the surroundings which

are at a temperature t_s. Show that the temperature t in the wire at a distance x from the section is given by the expression

$$\frac{t - t_s}{t_0 - t_s} = \frac{e^{\mu(l - x)} + e^{-\mu(l - x)}}{e^{\mu l} + e^{-\mu l}}$$

where μ^2 is Ep/kA, E is the surface heat transfer coefficient from the wire to the surrounding fluid, and k is the thermal conductivity of the wire. (*University of Glasgow*).

6. Show that the rate of heat transfer per unit width from a straight fin of uniform rectangular cross-section is given by

$$q = kmdt_0 \tanh ml$$

where k is the thermal conductivity, $m = \sqrt{(2h/kd)}$, h is the surface coefficient, d is the fin thickness, t_0 is the base temperature difference and l is the length. Neglect heat flow through the tip.

Fins of this type project from a plane wall at 10·2 cm intervals. Each fin is 1·27 cm thick and 15·2 cm long. Assuming the same surface coefficient of 45·5 J/m^2 s deg C, find the ratio of the heat loss from this wall to that from a plane wall at the same temperature. (Take $k = 43·3$ J/m s deg C). (Ans.: 2·37 to 1.) (*University of Manchester*).

REFERENCES

1. Jakob, M. *Heat Transfer*, Vol. 1, John Wiley and Sons, Inc., New York (1949).
2. Eckert, E. R. G., and Drake, R. M. *Heat and Mass Transfer*, McGraw-Hill Book Company, Inc., New York (1959).
3. Chapman, A. J. *Heat Transfer*, The Macmillan Company, New York (1960).

13

Heat exchangers

Much of the basic conduction and convection theory finds its greatest application in the heat exchanger. Whenever it is necessary to transfer enthalpy from one fluid to another in large quantities, some form of heat exchanger is used. The most common form of heat exchanger is that in which two fluid streams pass through in steady flow, and heat transfer takes place through a separating wall. Mechanisms involved are therefore convection to or from the solid surface and conduction through the wall. The wall surfaces may be finned to increase the overall heat transfer coefficient. Radiation is present if the temperature difference between the wall and fluid is large, but radiation effects are neglected in the following discussion. Another type of heat exchanger is the regenerator. Fluid flow is unsteady, and alternating. Its use is restricted to gases, since the hot and cold fluids alternately occupy the same space in the regenerator. The hot fluid transfers its energy to some packing, it is then displaced by the cold fluid which then receives energy from the packing. In some heat exchange requirements it so happens that mixing of the two fluid streams is useful and this gives rise to the third type of exchanger. Cooling towers and jet condensers in steam power plant are examples. In the cooling tower large quantities of water are cooled partly by evaporation of some of the water and partly by mixing with a colder air, so that mass transfer processes are also important.

This chapter is concerned only with the heat exchanger in which fluids are separated. The basic principles will be considered in relation to the simplest types only.

13.1. Types of Heat Exchanger, and Definitions

The two basic types of heat exchanger are the in-line or uni-directional flow exchanger and the cross-flow exchanger. Flow is along the same axis in the in-line exchanger, but the two fluids may flow in the same or opposite directions giving rise to the names parallel and counter flow. The in-line exchanger may consist simply of two concentric tubes, one fluid flowing in the inner tube and the other in the annulus. Alternatively, there may be a number of tubes within a large tube or shell and to increase heat transfer the shell fluid is made to flow partly across the tubes by means of baffles. More complicated arrangements exist. For example, the fluid flowing in the tubes can be reversed to flow back through another set of tubes all within the same shell. These examples are illustrated in Fig. 13.1. Figure 13.2 shows a water-cooled oil cooler in part section. Water flows through the tubes and makes two passes. Oil flows over the outside of the tubes in a single pass. The oil flow within the shell is controlled by the baffles, which are of the 'disc and doughnut' type.

The cross-flow exchanger is, as its name implies, one in which the two fluid streams flow at right angles. Gas-to-gas heat exchangers

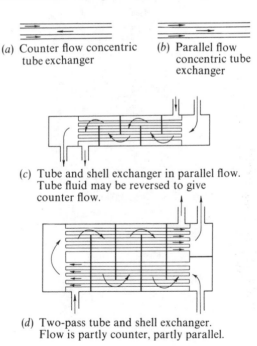

(a) Counter flow concentric tube exchanger

(b) Parallel flow concentric tube exchanger

(c) Tube and shell exchanger in parallel flow. Tube fluid may be reversed to give counter flow.

(d) Two-pass tube and shell exchanger. Flow is partly counter, partly parallel.

Fig. 13.1.   Basic in-line heat exchangers.

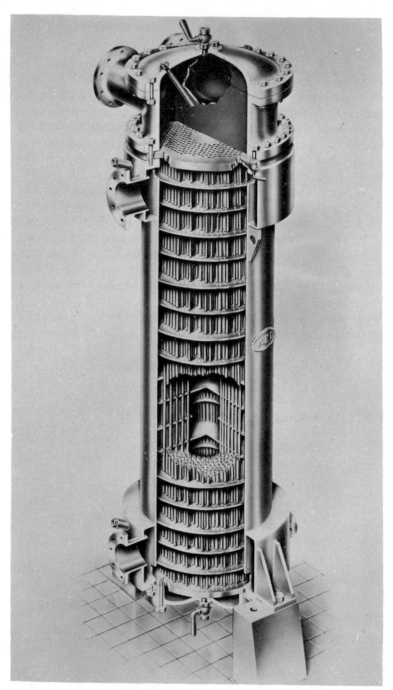

Fig. 13.2. *A liquid/liquid shell and tube heat exchanger. This type of unit is used for cooling transformer oil, with water as the cooling medium. Pressure drops: oil flow in the shell, 5–12 psi, water flow in the tubes, 1–5 psi. The heat transfer area is in the range 110–1090 ft^2, and the heat transfer rate is in the range 70–1950 kW. Photograph by courtesy of Associated Electrical Industries Limited.*

are often of this type. Their analysis is complicated because fluid temperatures vary in both the direction of flow and at right angles to that direction.

The temperature variations of the fluids in parallel and counter flow are shown in Fig. 13.3. Temperatures are plotted against length or area of heat exchanger surface. The inlet end, where length or area is zero is regarded as being the end where the hotter of the two fluids enters. The fluids are regarded as being hot or cold, for convenience, and t_h is a temperature of the hot fluid, t_c a temperature of the cold fluid. Suffixes 1 and 2 are used for inlet and outlet of individual streams, and θ_i is the temperature difference between fluids at the inlet end and θ_o the difference at the outlet end of the exchanger. An important term in heat exchanger theory is the *capacity ratio C*. It is a ratio of the products of mass flow rate and

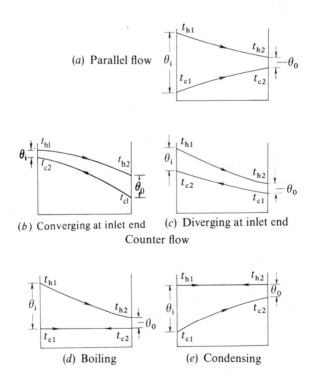

(a) Parallel flow

(b) Converging at inlet end   (c) Diverging at inlet end
Counter flow

(d) Boiling   (e) Condensing

Fig. 13.3.   *Temperature distributions*.

specific heat of each stream. It is always the ratio of the smaller product to the larger, since they are not necessarily equal. Thus, if $m_h c_{ph}$ is the 'capacity' of the hot stream and $m_c c_{pc}$ is that of the cold stream, then

if $m_h c_{ph} > m_c c_{pc}$,

$$C = \frac{m_c c_{pc}}{m_h c_{ph}} \tag{13.1}$$

and if $m_h c_{ph} < m_c c_{pc}$,

$$C = \frac{m_h c_{ph}}{m_c c_{pc}} \tag{13.2}$$

In counter flow, the temperature distributions are rather different depending on the capacity ratio. Thus, in Fig. 13.3b, the temperatures are converging at the inlet end when $m_h c_{ph} > m_c c_{pc}$ and equation (13.1) applies. In Fig. 13.3c the temperatures are diverging at the inlet end when $m_c c_{pc} > m_h c_{ph}$ and equation (13.2) applies.

In parallel flow it is obvious that t_{c2} will approach t_{h2} for an infinitely long heat exchanger, but can never exceed t_{h2}. In counter flow it is quite normal for t_{c2} to exceed t_{h2} and, consequently, the counter flow exchanger is the more 'effective'. *Effectiveness* is the ratio of energy actually transferred to the maximum theoretically possible. Again, the definition depends on the relative thermal capacities of the streams. The maximum theoretical transfer will take place in counter flow in an exchanger of infinite length and, in such a case, $t_{c2} \to t_{h1}$ when $m_h c_{ph} > m_c c_{pc}$, and $t_{h2} \to t_{c1}$ when $m_h c_{ph} < m_c c_{pc}$. Thus the maximum transfers in the two cases are:

$$m_c c_{pc}(t_{h1} - t_{c1}) \quad \text{when} \quad m_h c_{ph} > m_c c_{pc}$$

$$m_h c_{ph}(t_{h1} - t_{c1}) \quad \text{when} \quad m_h c_{ph} < m_c c_{pc}$$

The actual transfers in the two cases are $m_c c_{pc}(t_{c2} - t_{c1})$ and $m_h c_{ph}(t_{h1} - t_{h2})$, and hence E, the effectiveness, becomes

$$E = \frac{t_{c2} - t_{c1}}{t_{h1} - t_{c1}} \quad \text{when} \quad m_h c_{ph} > m_c c_{pc} \tag{13.3}$$

and

$$E = \frac{t_{h1} - t_{h2}}{t_{h1} - t_{c1}} \quad \text{when} \quad m_h c_{ph} < m_c c_{pc} \tag{13.4}$$

These definitions may be used in either counter or parallel flow, but the value of E will be lower in parallel flow.

Temperature distributions with a change of phase are also shown in Fig. 13.3. These will occur in boiling, Fig. 13.3d, and condensing, Fig. 13.3e. Only the phase change takes place in the exchanger, so the temperature of the boiling or condensing fluid does not change. The temperature distributions are the same for both parallel and counter flow. The capacity ratio C becomes 0 for both boiling and condensing since the larger thermal capacity is in each case infinite. This follows, since by definition, $c_p = dh/dt$ $= \infty$ when $dt = 0$. Equations (13.3) and (13.4) may be used in condensing and boiling, respectively.

The other limit of capacity ratio is $C = 1$ and occurs when the thermal capacities of the two streams are equal. This is not illustrated, but it results in the temperature distributions being parallel straight lines in the case of counter flow, θ being a constant over the whole heat exchange area.

13.2. Determination of Heat Exchanger Performance

The primary purpose of a heat exchanger is to achieve the required transfer rate using the smallest possible transfer area and fluid pressure drop. A large exchanger can mean unnecessary capital outlay and high pressure drop means a reduced efficiency of the plant considered overall. Generally, a smaller exchanger can be produced by finning surfaces to increase the overall heat transfer coefficient. However, this leads to a higher fluid pressure drop, and the best design is often a compromise between conflicting requirements. In fact, a number of different designs for a given duty may be acceptable.

The heat transfer requirement, Q, can be expressed in three ways:

$$Q = U_A A \theta_m = U_L L \theta_m \tag{13.5}$$

$$Q = m_c c_{pc}(t_{c2} - t_{c1}) \tag{13.6}$$

$$Q = m_h c_{ph}(t_{h1} - t_{h2}) \tag{13.7}$$

θ_m is a mean temperature difference between the fluids, and U_A and U_L are mean coefficients, in watt/m^2 deg C and watt/m deg C or equivalent units applicable over the entire area A or length L

of the exchanger. It is general practice to work in terms of the external surface area of the tubes in heat exchanger design, and the overall coefficient U_A in terms of this area is given by equations (12.21) for finned surfaces and (12.22) for plain surfaces.

13.2.1. Counter and Parallel Flow. If the mass flow rates and inlet and outlet temperatures are known, the heat transfer Q will be known, but further details of the exchanger cannot be specified until θ_m is known. θ_m can be derived as follows:

Consider an incremental area of heat exchanger surface as shown for either counter or parallel flow in Fig. 13.4. The heat transfer over the area dA can be expressed in three ways as before, thus

$$dQ = U_A \, dA\theta \tag{13.8}$$

$$dQ = m_c c_{pc} \, dt_c \tag{13.9}$$

$$dQ = m_h c_{ph} \, dt_h \tag{13.10}$$

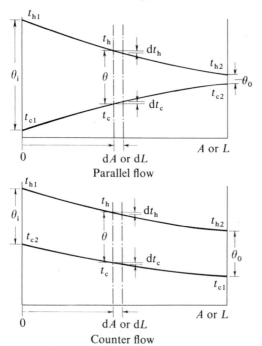

Fig. 13.4. *For the determination of logarithmic mean temperature difference.*

The temperature difference at the point in question is

$$\theta = t_h - t_c$$

and the increment in temperature difference is

$$d\theta = d(t_h - t_c)$$
$$= dt_h - dt_c \qquad (13.11)$$

If $d\theta$ is expressed in terms of dQ from (13.9) and (13.10),

$$d\theta = -\frac{dQ}{m_h c_{ph}} - \frac{dQ}{m_c c_{pc}} \quad \text{for parallel flow} \qquad (13.12)$$

and

$$d\theta = -\frac{dQ}{m_h c_{ph}} + \frac{dQ}{m_c c_{pc}} \quad \text{for counter flow} \qquad (13.13)$$

since dt_h is negative in both cases, and dt_c is positive for parallel flow and negative for counter flow. It follows that $d\theta/dQ$ has constant but different values for parallel and counter flow, and therefore

$$\frac{\theta_o - \theta_i}{Q} = -\left(\frac{1}{m_h c_{ph}} \pm \frac{1}{m_c c_{pc}}\right) \qquad (13.14)$$

with $+$ for parallel flow and $-$ for counter flow. Further, dQ from equation (13.8) may be substituted in (13.12) and (13.13) to give

$$\frac{d\theta}{\theta} = -\left(\frac{1}{m_h c_{ph}} \pm \frac{1}{m_c c_{pc}}\right) U \, dA$$

This is integrated from 0 to A to give

$$\ln\frac{\theta_o}{\theta_i} = -\left(\frac{1}{m_h c_{ph}} \pm \frac{1}{m_c c_{pc}}\right) U_A A \qquad (13.15)$$

The term in parentheses is now eliminated between (13.15) and (13.14) to give

$$Q = U_A A \frac{\theta_o - \theta_i}{\ln(\theta_o/\theta_i)} \qquad (13.16)$$

This result is clearly identical in form to equation (13.5) and it is seen that

$$\theta_m = \frac{\theta_o - \theta_i}{\ln (\theta_o/\theta_i)} \tag{13.17}$$

This is the required logarithmic mean temperature difference. It is the same for counter and parallel flow, though θ_o and θ_i in terms of values of t_h and t_c are different as can be seen from Fig. 13.3.

EXAMPLE 13.1

0·2 kg/s of an alcohol is to be cooled from 75 to 35°C in a counter flow heat exchanger. Cooling water enters the exchanger at 12°C and at the rate of 0·16 kg/s. The convection coefficient between the alcohol and the tube wall is 340 watt/m² deg C, and between the tube wall and the water, 225 watt/m² deg C. The tubes may be assumed thin. c_p for the alcohol is 2520 joule/kg deg C and for water is 4186·8 joule/kg deg C.

Calculate the capacity ratio, the effectiveness, and the area of the heat exchanger surface.

Solution. For the hot stream, alcohol,

$$m_h c_{ph} = 0·2 \times 2520 = 504 \text{ joule/s deg C}$$

For the cold stream, water,

$$m_c c_{pc} = 0·16 \times 4186·8 = 671 \text{ joule/s deg C}$$

From equation (13.2), $C = m_h c_{ph}/m_c c_{pc} = 504/671 = 0·75$. An energy balance gives

$$0·2 \times 2520 \times (75 - 35) = 0·16 \times 4186·8 \times (t_{c2} - 12)$$

$$20{,}150 = 671 t_{c2} - 8050$$

$$\therefore \quad t_{c2} = 41·8°C$$

From equation (13.4),

$$E = \frac{t_{h1} - t_{h2}}{t_{h1} - t_{c1}} = \frac{75 - 35}{75 - 12} = 0·635$$

The heat exchange area may be found from equation (13.5). To find

$$\theta_m: \qquad \theta_o = 35 - 12 = 23, \qquad \theta_i = 75 - 41\cdot8 = 33\cdot2$$

$$\therefore \quad \theta_m = \frac{23 - 33\cdot2}{\ln(23/33\cdot2)} = \frac{-10\cdot2}{-\ln 1\cdot44} = 28 \text{ deg C}$$

Since the tubes are thin, $r_1 = r_2$ in (12.22), so U_A is given by

$$\frac{1}{U_A} = \frac{1}{h_{alcohol}} + \frac{1}{h_{water}} = \frac{1}{340} + \frac{1}{225}$$

$$\therefore \qquad U_A = 135\cdot5 \text{ watt/m}^2 \text{ deg C}$$

Equation (13.5) gives $20{,}150 = U_A A \theta_m = 135\cdot5 \times A \times 28$

$$\therefore \qquad A = 5\cdot31 \text{ m}^2$$

13.2.2. Cross Flow. Analysis of the cross-flow heat exchanger is more complicated owing to temperature variation across the flow. This variation will depend on whether the fluid is *mixed* or *unmixed*. A mixed fluid is free to move across the flow direction; an unmixed fluid is constrained in parallel flow passages. Thus, if an exchanger consisted of a bank of tubes placed across a duct, the fluid in the duct would be mixed while the fluid in the tubes would be unmixed.

Results of analyses of this type of exchanger are available as correction factors.[1,2] Equation (13.5) would become

$$Q = U_A A F \theta_m$$

where F is a factor to be obtained from the appropriate graph, and θ_m is the mean temperature difference, (13.17), calculated for counter flow with the same inlet and outlet temperatures as for cross flow. Figure 13.5 shows F for a cross-flow exchanger with one fluid mixed and one fluid unmixed. In applying the factor F it does not matter whether the hotter fluid is mixed or unmixed.

13.3. Heat Exchanger Transfer Units

One would now expect to be able to go ahead and design a heat exchanger, using equations (13.5) to (13.7) and information from earlier chapters to evaluate U_A for the particular configuration in mind. However, U_A cannot be determined until something is

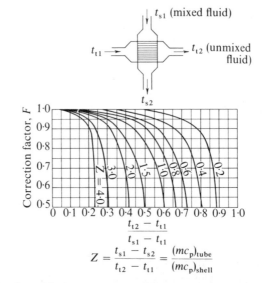

Fig. 13.5. *Logarithmic temperature difference correction factor for cross flow, one fluid mixed, one fluid unmixed. From R. A. Bowman, A. E. Mueller, and W. M. Nagle. Trans. ASME, Vol. 62, p. 283 (1940). By permission of the American Society of Mechanical Engineers.*

known of the tube sizes and velocities of flow, and the method of procedure from theory so far developed can be extremely involved and iterative. For example, supposing the tube sizes, length and U_A were decided upon, in order to check the design performance the value of Q and outlet temperatures of the fluids must be regarded as unknowns and equations (13.5) to (13.7) cannot be solved directly for Q, t_{c2}, and t_{h2}, because of the logarithmic form of θ_m. The approach using transfer units is very useful from this point of view. The method was developed by Kays and London.[3]

The effectiveness E, and capacity ratio C of a heat exchanger have already been defined. These quantities will now be used in conjunction with a new term, Number of Transfer Units, NTU, to determine heat exchanger performance. As with E and C, the definition of NTU depends on the relative magnitudes of the thermal capacities of the fluid stream. Thus,

$$NTU = \frac{U_A A}{m_c c_{pc}}, \qquad \text{when } m_h c_{ph} > m_c c_{pc} \qquad (13.18)$$

and,

$$NTU = \frac{U_A A}{m_h c_{ph}}, \quad \text{when } m_h c_{ph} < m_c c_{pc} \tag{13.19}$$

Thus the denominator is always the smaller thermal capacity. The performance of heat exchangers will now be examined using the definitions of C, E, and NTU in equations (13.1) to (13.4) and (13.18) and (13.19).

13.3.1. Counter Flow Exchanger.

Let $m_h c_{ph}$ be assumed the smaller quantity, then the definitions of NTU, C, and E are

$$NTU = \frac{U_A A}{m_h c_{ph}}, \quad C = \frac{m_h c_{ph}}{m_c c_{pc}}, \quad E = \frac{t_{h1} - t_{h2}}{t_{h1} - t_{c1}}$$

Equations (13.9) and (13.10) for counter flow (where temperature increments are negative) give

$$- m_c c_{pc}\, dt_c = - m_h c_{ph}\, dt_h = dQ \tag{13.20}$$

Now, $d\theta = d(t_h - t_c) = dt_h - dt_c$,

and $m_h c_{ph}(dt_h - dt_c) = dt_c(m_c c_{pc} - m_h c_{ph})$

using equation (13.20). Again, using (13.20), dt_c may be eliminated to give

$$m_h c_{ph}(dt_h - dt_c) = -\frac{dQ}{m_c c_{pc}}(m_c c_{pc} - m_h c_{ph})$$

$$= -dQ(1 - C)$$

Using equation (13.8) to eliminate dQ gives

$$dt_h - dt_c = -\frac{U_A\, dA\theta}{m_h c_{ph}}(1 - C)$$

$$\therefore \quad \frac{d\theta}{\theta} = -\frac{U_A\, dA}{m_h c_{ph}}(1 - C)$$

Integrating:

$$\ln\frac{\theta_o}{\theta_i} = \ln\frac{t_{h2} - t_{c1}}{t_{h1} - t_{c2}} = -\frac{U_A A}{m_h c_{ph}}(1 - C)$$

$$= -NTU(1 - C)$$

$$\therefore \quad \frac{t_{h2} - t_{c1}}{t_{h1} - t_{c2}} = e^{-NTU(1 - C)}$$

The left-hand side of this equation may be manipulated as follows:

$$\frac{t_{h2} - t_{c1}}{t_{h1} - t_{c2}} = \frac{t_{h1} - t_{c1} - (t_{h1} - t_{h2})}{t_{h1} - t_{c1} - (t_{c2} - t_{c1})}$$

$$= \frac{t_{h1} - t_{c1} - (t_{h1} - t_{h2})}{t_{h1} - t_{c1} - C(t_{h1} - t_{h2})}, \quad \text{(using the definition of } C\text{)}$$

$$= \frac{1 - \dfrac{t_{h1} - t_{h2}}{t_{h1} - t_{c1}}}{1 - \dfrac{C(t_{h1} - t_{h2})}{(t_{h1} - t_{c1})}}$$

$$= \frac{1 - E}{1 - CE} = e^{-NTU(1-C)}$$

from the right-hand side, above. This final result is now rearranged to give

$$E = \frac{1 - e^{-NTU(1-C)}}{1 - C e^{-NTU(1-C)}} \qquad (13.21)$$

If $m_c c_{pc}$ had been assumed the smaller quantity, the same equation would have been obtained, where E, NTU, and C would have then been defined by the alternative expressions.

A relationship exists, then, between E, NTU, and C given by equation (13.21). Using this result it is possible to determine outlet temperatures t_{c2} and t_{h2}, and Q, the overall heat transfer for a given design, without using a trial and error solution.

EXAMPLE 13.2

Determine the performance of an oil cooler handling 3850 lb/h of oil at an inlet temperature of 130°C. The mean specific heat is 0·53. 2550 lb/h of water entering at 15°C passes in counter flow. The surface area is 21·5 ft² and the overall heat transfer coefficient is known to be 180 Chu/ft² h deg C.

Solution. The thermal capacities are: oil, $3850 \times 0·53 = 2040$ Chu/h deg C, water $= 2550$ Chu/h deg C

$$\therefore \quad C = 2040/2550 = 0·80$$

and,

$$NTU = \frac{180 \times 21 \cdot 5}{2040} = 1 \cdot 9$$

Then,

$$E = \frac{t_{h1} - t_{h2}}{t_{h1} - t_{c1}} = \frac{1 - e^{-1 \cdot 9(1 - 0 \cdot 8)}}{1 - 0 \cdot 8\, e^{-1 \cdot 9(1 - 0 \cdot 8)}}$$

$$= \frac{1 - e^{-0 \cdot 38}}{1 - 0 \cdot 8\, e^{-0 \cdot 38}} = \frac{0 \cdot 316}{0 \cdot 453} = 0 \cdot 696$$

$$= \frac{130° - t_{h2}}{130° - 15°}$$

$$\therefore \quad t_{h2} = 49 \cdot 8°C \quad \text{(oil outlet)}$$

By enthalpy balance

$$(t_{c2} - t_{c1}) = \frac{2040 \times (130 - 49 \cdot 8)}{2550} = 64 \text{ deg C}$$

$$\therefore \quad t_{c2} = 79°C \quad \text{(water outlet)}$$

The total heat transfer is 163,500 Chu/h.

An alternative problem would have been to calculate the area necessary for specified outlet temperatures.

When U_A is not known, this must be determined from either equation (12.21) or (12.22), with the individual convection coefficients determined from the equation appropriate to the fluid, flow geometry and type of flow, as given in earlier chapters. It is convenient to use standard tube sizes to give a suitable value of Re and number of tubes for the specified mass flow. Several attempts may be necessary to achieve a suitable U_A combined with a fluid pressure loss which is acceptable.

13.3.2. Parallel Flow Exchanger. A similar analysis in parallel flow will yield the result

$$E = \frac{1 - e^{-NTU(1 + C)}}{1 + C} \tag{13.22}$$

Again this result is independent of which fluid stream has the smaller thermal capacity, provided the appropriate definitions of E, NTU, and C are used.

13.3.3. Limiting Values of C. It has already been noted that $C = 0$ in both condensing and boiling. When this is so both equation (13.21) and (13.22) reduce to

$$E = 1 - e^{-NTU} \qquad (13.23)$$

Thus, the effectiveness is the same for both counter and parallel flow.

The other limiting value is $C = 1$ for equal thermal capacities and, in this case, for parallel flow equation (13.22) gives

$$E = \frac{1 - e^{-2NTU}}{2} \qquad (13.24)$$

In the case of counter flow for $C = 1$ it is necessary to do a fresh analysis from first principles since equation (13.21) becomes indeterminant. For this case it is possible to write

$$E = (t_{h1} - t_{h2})/(t_{h1} - t_{c1})$$

and also

$$(t_{h1} - t_{h2}) = (t_{c2} - t_{c1})$$

Also

$$Q = U_A A(t_{h1} - t_{c2}) = mc_p(t_{h1} - t_{h2})$$

$$\therefore \quad (t_{h1} - t_{h2}) = NTU(t_{h1} - t_{c2})$$

E may be written as

$$E = \frac{t_{h1} - t_{h2}}{(t_{h1} - t_{h2}) - (t_{c1} - t_{h2})} = \frac{(t_{h1} - t_{c2})NTU}{(t_{h1} - t_{c2})NTU - (t_{c1} - t_{h2})}$$

But $(t_{c1} - t_{h2}) = -(t_{h1} - t_{c2})$

$$\therefore \quad E = \frac{NTU}{NTU + 1}, \quad \text{when } C = 1 \qquad (13.25)$$

13.3.4. Cross-Flow Exchanger.

Convenient graphical plots of effectiveness as a function of NTU and capacity ratio are available for cross flow. Figure 13.6 is for one fluid mixed and one fluid unmixed. When the capacity ratio of mixed to unmixed fluid is greater than 1, the NTU is then based on (mc_p) of the unmixed fluid.

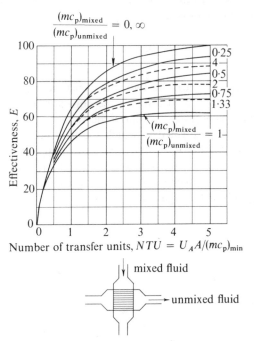

Fig. 13.6.   *Effectiveness vs. NTU for a cross-flow exchanger, one fluid mixed, one fluid unmixed. From Compact Heat Exchangers, by W. M. Kays and A. L. London, McGraw-Hill Book Company, Inc., New York (1958). Used by permission of McGraw-Hill Book Company.*

13.4. Determination of Heat Transfer Coefficients from Heat Exchanger Tests

The measurement of forced convection coefficients is an important part of heat transfer work, whether it is simply a check on a designed performance, or an investigation on a new system. This generally involves some form of heat exchanger equipment, in which an overall coefficient between two fluids is measured. The method of Wilson[4] enables an individual film coefficient to be determined from the overall measurement. The method was developed primarily to keep a check on the effect of surface deposits on the performance of condensers, but it also has general application.

The overall resistance to heat transfer between the two fluid streams may be expressed as

$$\frac{1}{U} = R_{f1} + R_w + R_{f2}$$

where R_{f1} and R_{f2} are the two film resistances and R_w the wall conduction resistance. If $1/R_{f1}$ is the convection coefficient to be determined, it is necessary to know the value of $R_w + R_{f2}$. A series of tests may be performed in which the flow velocity of fluid 2 is kept constant, so that R_{f2} is essentially constant over the test series. R_{f1} will vary with the mass flow rate of fluid 1, and for turbulent flow $1/R_{f1}$ may be assumed to be proportional to $v_{m1}^{0.8}$. The Wilson plot is a graph of $1/U$ against $1/v_{m1}^{0.8}$, as in Fig. 13.7. When $1/v_{m1}^{0.8}$ is

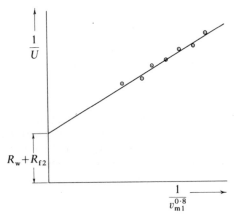

Fig. 13.7. The Wilson plot.

extrapolated to zero, the value of $1/U$ obtained will comprise $R_w + R_{f2}$ only, since the film resistance R_{f1} is zero, or the convection coefficient is infinite, at an infinite value of v_{m1}. By this means the constant value of $R_w + R_{f2}$ is determined, and this may now be subtracted from all experimental values of $1/U$ in order to obtain R_{f1} for each test.

PROBLEMS

1. A tubular heater of the counter flow type is used to heat 10,000 lb/h of fuel oil of specific heat 0·75 from 50 to 80°F. Heat is supplied by means of 12,000 lb/h of water which enters the heater at 180°F.

(a) Derive an equation relating the temperatures of oil and water at any section of the heater.

(b) Determine the necessary surface if the rate of heat transfer is 200 in Btu, ft, h, deg F units. (Ans.: 10·9 ft².) (University College, London).

2. In a test on a steam condenser the rate of flow of cooling water was varied whilst the condensation temperature was maintained constant. The following results were obtained:

| Overall heat transfer coefficient K, J/m² s deg C | 2700 | 2980 | 3390 | 3590 |
| Water velocity V, m/s | 0·986 | 1·27 | 1·83 | 2·16 |

Assuming the surface coefficient on the water side to be proportional to $V^{0.8}$, determine from an appropriate graph, the mean value of the steam side surface coefficient. The thickness of the metal wall is 0·122 cm and thermal conductivity of tube material 111 J/m s deg C. (Ans.: 6040 J/m² s deg C.) (University of Manchester).

3. Oil is cooled by water in a parallel-flow heat exchanger. The water enters at a temperature of 60°F and is heated to 120°F. The oil is cooled from 270 to 150°F. Neglecting heat loss from the exchanger and stating any assumptions made, determine

(a) the minimum temperature to which the oil may be cooled;

(b) the exit temperature of each stream if the water flow direction were reversed;

(c) the lowest temperature to which the oil could be cooled with counter-flow operation;

(d) the ratio of the required exchanger length for parallel flow to that for counter flow to induce an oil outlet temperature of 150°F, inlet conditions and flow rates being unaltered. [Ans.: (a) 130°F, (b) 134°, 128°F, (c) 60°F, (d) 1·26 to 1.] (University College, London).

4. (i) Define the term 'mean temperature difference' as applied to a heat exchanger and show that, for a counter flow heat exchanger, it is given by

$$\Delta t_m = \frac{\Delta t_2 - \Delta t_1}{\ln (\Delta t_2/\Delta t_1)}$$

where Δt_m is the mean temperature difference, Δt_1 is the temperature difference between the two fluids at one end of the heat exchanger, and Δt_2 is the temperature difference at the other end. State any necessary assumptions.

(ii) A tubular, counter flow oil cooler is to use a supply of cold water as the cooling fluid. Using the following data, calculate the mean temperature difference and the required surface area of the tubes.

Data:	Oil	Water
Entry temperature, °C	121	15·6
Exit temperature, °C	82·3	—
Mass flow rate, kg/s	0·189	0·378
Specific heat, J/kg deg C	2094	4187

Mean overall coefficient of heat transfer, referred to outside surface of tubes, 454 J/m² s deg C. (Ans.: 80·0 deg C, 0·422 m².) (*Imperial College, London*).

5. A brine cooler consists of twenty pipes each 5 ft length and 1 in. bore. The wall thickness is $\frac{1}{16}$ in. and each pipe runs concentrically in a larger pipe so that cooling water can flow in the annular space so created.

Brine at 65°F passes at a rate of 200 lb/h counter current to water at 40°F and 400 lb/h. Assuming an overall average heat transfer coefficient of 25 Btu/ft² h deg F and specific heat of both brine and water 1·0 Btu/lb deg F calculate the outlet temperatures. (Ans.: Brine 42·2°F, water 51·2°F.) (*University of Manchester*).

6. Water is to be heated from 70 to 90°F by passing it through a steel tube 1·0 in. inside diameter, 0·125 in. thick with steam condensing on the outside at 1·69 lb/in². The water velocity is 12 ft/s and the properties of the water at the mean temperature are: $k = 0·349$ Btu/ft h deg F; $\mu = 2·10$ lb/ft h; $\rho = 62·2$ lb/ft³.

Assuming that the surface heat transfer coefficient for the steam side is 1000 Btu/ft² h deg F and the thermal conductivity of the steel is 25 Btu/ft h deg F, find the overall heat transfer coefficient referred to the outside surface of the tube, and the length of the tube required.

For the water side take $Nu = 0·023(Re)^{0·8}(Pr)^{0·4}$. (Ans.: 485 Btu/ft² h deg F, 47·4 ft.) (*Queen Mary College, London*).

7. An oil cooler consists of a straight tube, of inside diameter 1·27 cm, wall thickness 0·127 cm enclosed within a pipe and concentric with it. The external surface of the pipe is well lagged.

Oil flow through the tube at the rate of 0·063 kg/s and cooling water flows in the annulus between the tube and the pipe at the rate of 0·0756 kg/s and in the direction opposite to that of the oil. The oil enters the tube at 177°C and is cooled to 65·5°C. The cooling water enters at 10°C.

Estimate the length of tube required, given that the heat transfer coefficient from oil to tube surface is 1700 J/m² s deg C, and that from the surface to water is 3970 J/m² s deg C. Neglect the temperature drop across the tube wall. The specific heat of the oil is 1675 J/kg deg C. (Ans.: 2·67 m.) (*University of London*).

8. A tank contains 500 lb of water which is to be raised in temperature from 60 to 200°F in 45 min by heat transfer from a submerged coil of $1\frac{1}{4}$ in. outside diameter pipe in which steam condenses. The coefficient of heat transfer

between the surface of the pipe and the water in the tank is 90 Btu/ft² h deg F and is constant. The surface temperature of the pipe is assumed constant at 280°F. The water in the tank is well stirred. Determine the length of pipe required, deriving any formulae used and stating your assumptions. (Ans.: 22·9 ft.) (*University of London*).

9. Explain briefly what is meant by the term 'surface or film coefficient' in heat transfer considerations.

A counter-flow heat exchanger having an overall heat transfer coefficient of 114 J/m² s deg C is used to heat to 329°C the air entering the combustion chamber of a gas turbine cycle. The pressure ratio of the cycle is 5:1 and the heating fluid is the exhaust from the turbine which expands the gas from 650°C with an isentropic efficiency of 82 per cent. If the air conditions initially are 101·3 kN/m² and 21°C and the isentropic efficiency of the compressor is 80 per cent, calculate the area of heat exchanger for a total fluid mass flow of 22·7 kg/s.

Assume a logarithmic mean temperature difference and constant specific heat of 1000 for the air and 1090 J/kg deg C for the products. $\gamma = 1·4$ for air and products. (Ans.: 424 m².) (*University of Manchester*).

10. In a cross-flow heat exchanger, heat is transferred from a hot gas flowing in a single shell pass to a colder gas flowing in multiple tube passes. Discuss the conditions under which the mean temperature difference of such a system approaches the logarithmic mean temperature difference for a simple counter-flow process having the same terminal temperatures.

The secondary section of a divided convective superheater in a 2450 lbf/in² boiler is required to raise the steam temperature from 750 to 850°F. The steam flow rate is $1·4 \times 10^6$ lbm/h, whilst the combustion products at an initial temperature of 1400°F flow through the single shell pass at $1·25 \times 10^6$ lbm/h. If the mean temperature difference for this heat exchanger is 0·92 of the log mean temperature difference for the corresponding counter-flow system, calculate, using the additional data given below, the area of the superheater surface.

Mean specific heat of combustion products, 0·25.
Surface coefficient on steam side, 150 Btu/ft² h deg F.
Surface coefficient on gas side, 16 Btu/ft² h deg F.
(Ans.: 26,700 ft².) (*University of Manchester*).

11. Define the terms 'effectiveness' and 'number of transfer units' as applied to heat exchangers stating any assumptions involved. Obtain a relationship between effectiveness and number of transfer units for a counter-current heat exchanger and plot this relationship when the ratio of the stream heat capacities is 0·5.

20·15 kg/s of an oil fraction at a temperature of 121°C is to be cooled in a simple counter-current heat exchanger using 5·04 kg/s of water initially at 10°C. The exchanger contains 200 tubes each 4·87 m long and 1·97 cm outside diameter; the resulting heat transfer coefficient referred to the outside tube area is 340 J/m² s deg C. If the specific heat of the oil is 2094 J/kg deg C calculate the exit temperature of the oil. (Ans.: 90·8°C.) (*University of Leeds*).

REFERENCES

1. Smith, D. M. *Engineering*, Vol. 138, 479, 606 (1934).
2. Bowman, R. A., Mueller, A. C., and Nagle, W. M. *Trans. ASME*, Vol. 62, 283 (1940).
3. Kays, W. M., and London, A. L. *Compact Heat Exchangers*, McGraw-Hill Book Company, Inc., New York (1964).
4. Wilson, E. E. *Trans. ASME*, Vol. 37, 47 (1915).

Section 4
Heat Transfer by Radiation

14

The laws of black- and grey-body radiation

The processes of heat transfer considered so far have been intimately related to the nature of the material medium, the presence of solid–fluid interfaces, and the presence of fluid motion. Energy transfer has been observed to take place only in the direction of a negative temperature gradient, and at a rate which depends directly on the magnitude of that gradient.

It is now necessary to consider the third mode of heat transfer which is characteristically different from conduction and convection. Radiation occurs most freely in a vacuum, it is freely transmitted in air (though partially absorbed by other gases) and, in general, is partially reflected and partially absorbed by solids. Transmission of radiation, which can occur in solids as well as fluids, is an interesting phenomenon because it can occur through a cold non-absorbing medium between two other hotter bodies. Thus the surface of the earth receives energy direct by radiation from the sun, even though the atmosphere at high altitude is extremely cold. Similarly, the glass of a green house is colder than the contents and radiant energy does not stop there, it is transmitted to the warmer absorbing surfaces inside. Radiation is also significantly different from conduction and convection in that the temperature level is a controlling factor. In furnaces and combustion chambers, radiation is the predominating mechanism of heat transfer.

As already mentioned in chapter 1, radiant energy is but part of the entire spectrum of electromagnetic radiation. All radiation travels at the speed of light and, consequently, longer wave-lengths correspond to lower frequencies, and shorter wave-lengths to higher frequencies. The entire spectrum of electromagnetic radiation extends from about 10^{-4} angstrom units (10^{-14} metres), the wavelength region of cosmic rays, up to about 20,000 metres, in the region of Hertzian or electric waves. The wave-length region generally associated with thermal radiation is 10^3–10^6 angstrom units, which includes some ultra-violet, all the visible, and some infra-red radiation.

Since radiation energy exchange depends on the rates at which energy is emitted by one body and absorbed by another, it is necessary to establish definitions relating to these characteristics of surfaces. Further, not all of the energy emitted by one body may necessarily fall on the surface of another due to their geometric arrangement, and this too must be investigated. This then forms the general approach by which engineers may consider radiant energy exchange.

14.1. Absorption and Reflection of Radiant Energy

Three possibilities may follow the incidence of radiation on a surface. Some may be reflected and some transmitted, leaving the body unaltered. The rest will have been absorbed, resulting generally in an increase in temperature of the body at the surface. On absorption, radiation has become internal energy of the body. This will then be distributed throughout the body according to the mechanisms of heat transfer already considered.

The percentage of incident energy absorbed by a surface is defined as α, the absorptivity; the percentage reflected is ρ, the reflectivity, and the percentage transmitted is τ, the transmissivity. Thus it must follow that

$$\alpha + \rho + \tau = 1 \qquad (14.1)$$

Energy absorbed on the surface is, in fact, absorbed in a finite thickness of material, and if the body is very thin less absorption and more transmission may take place. It will be assumed that 'thick' bodies only will be considered, for which $\tau = 0$. Hence

$$\alpha + \rho = 1 \qquad (14.2)$$

In engineering applications of radiation, there will generally be a gas separating solid bodies, and often this gas is air which may be assumed to have no absorptivity or reflectivity, so $\tau = 1$. Combustion gases containing carbon dioxide, water vapour, and incandescent carbon particles behave very differently, however, and radiation in furnaces is an important subject, but beyond the scope of this book.

14.2. Emission, Radiosity, and Irradiation

To be consistent with previous nomenclature, Q is the energy emitted by a surface in heat units per unit time. This energy emission results from the surface temperature and the nature of the surface. However, Q may not be the total energy leaving that surface, there may also be some reflected incident energy. Thus J is defined as the Radiosity, which is the total radiant energy leaving the surface, in unit time. Similarly, G is defined as the Irradiation which is total incident energy on a surface, some of which may be emission and some reflection from elsewhere.

If G is the incident energy, ρG will be reflected. Thus

$$J = Q + \rho G \tag{14.3}$$

14.3. Black and Non-Black Bodies

All materials have values of α and ρ between 0 and 1. However, it is useful and important to imagine a material for which $\alpha = 1$ and $\rho = 0$. A body composed of this material is known as a black body; it absorbs all incident energy upon it and reflects none. For real materials the highest values of α are around 0·97. Artificial surfaces may be arranged in practice which are virtually black. Consider Fig. 14.1. The hollow enclosure has an inside surface of high absorptivity. Incident energy passes through the small opening and is

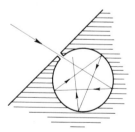

Fig. 14.1.   Artificial black-body surface.

absorbed on the inside surface. However, some is reflected, but most of this is absorbed on a second incidence. Again, a small fraction is reflected. After a number of such reflections the amount unabsorbed is exceedingly small and very little of the original incident energy is reflected back out of the opening. The area of the opening may thus be regarded as black.

The work of Stefan and Boltzmann led to the law named after them which gives the emission of radiant energy from a black body. Thus

$$Q_b = A\sigma T^4 \quad \text{or} \quad q_b = \sigma T^4 \tag{14.4}$$

is the Stefan–Boltzmann law for black-body radiation. T is the absolute temperature and σ is the Stefan–Boltzmann constant and has the values:

$$5{\cdot}663 \times 10^{-8} \text{ J/m}^2 \text{ s (deg K)}^4$$
$$0{\cdot}171 \times 10^{-8} \text{ Btu/ft}^2 \text{ h (deg R)}^4$$
$$1{\cdot}00 \times 10^{-8} \text{ Chu/ft}^2 \text{ h (deg K)}^4$$

A derivation of this law is given by Jakob.[1]

Black-body radiation consists of emission over the entire range of wave-length. Most of the energy is concentrated in the wave-length range already mentioned. The point to note is that the energy is not distributed uniformly over this range. Thus $q_{b\lambda}$ may be defined as the monochromatic emittance, the energy emitted per unit area at the wave-length λ, for a black body. It must follow that

$$q_b = \int_0^\infty q_{b\lambda}\,d\lambda = \sigma T^4 \tag{14.5}$$

The variation of monochromatic emittance with wave-length is shown in Fig. 14.2. The area under the curve is q_b.

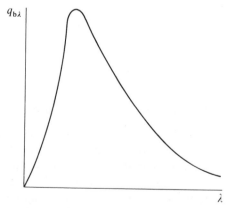

Fig. 14.2.   Distribution of monochromatic emittance for a black body.

Real materials that are not black will have monochromatic emittances that are different from $q_{b\lambda}$, and hence it is useful to define a monochromatic emissivity ε_λ by the equation

$$q_\lambda = \varepsilon_\lambda q_{b\lambda}$$

or

$$\varepsilon_\lambda = \frac{q_\lambda}{q_{b\lambda}} \qquad (14.6)$$

The black and non-black emittances which give ε_λ are measured at the same temperature. In general, ε_λ is a function of wave-length and temperature. There are two types of non-black body, known as selective emitters and grey bodies. Many real materials are selective emitters. This means that ε_λ does vary with wave-length in the manner of Fig. 14.3. An emittance that varies with wave-length is undesirable from the engineer's point of view and it is possible to

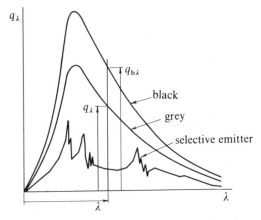

Fig. 14.3. *Comparison of the emission of black, grey, and selective emitting surfaces;* $\varepsilon_\lambda = q_\lambda/q_{b\lambda}$.

express the same total emission of a body in terms of a uniform value of ε, independent of λ. Such a body is called a grey body, and selective emitters with variable ε are sometimes referred to as non-grey. Grey-body emission is also shown in Fig. 14.3. It must follow that for a grey body

$$q = \varepsilon q_b = \varepsilon \sigma T^4 \qquad (14.7)$$

The value of ε used for a grey body is generally a function of the temperature of the surface, but again a simplifying assumption enables a suitable constant value to be used, irrespective of temperature, provided the range is not too large. Values of ε for real materials, and the temperatures at which they are valid, are given in Table A.6 (see p. 236).

It is now apparent that materials exist for which $\alpha < 1$ and also for which the emission is not equal to the black-body emission. By means of Kirchhoff's law the relationship between α and ε may be established.

14.4. Kirchhoff's Law[2]

Consider a small black body of area A_1 completely enclosed by a larger body with an internal black surface area A_2, as in Fig. 14.4.

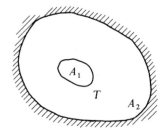

Fig. 14.4.   To demonstrate Kirchhoff's law.

Both surfaces are at the same temperature. The small body will emit at the rate $A_1 \sigma T^4$ and must also absorb energy at the same rate otherwise the temperature of the body will change. The concave surface A_2 will emit $A_2 \sigma T^4$, but only $A_1 \sigma T^4$ of this is incident upon, and absorbed by, A_1. If F is the fraction of energy leaving A_2 which is absorbed by A_1, then

$$F = \frac{A_1 \sigma T^4}{A_2 \sigma T^4} = \frac{A_1}{A_2} \tag{14.8}$$

The remainder of the energy emitted by A_2 will be re-absorbed by A_2 as it will miss A_1.

Now consider what happens when the black body of area A_1 is replaced by a grey body of identical dimensions, with an absorptivity of α and an emissivity of ε, the temperature throughout remaining at T. Since there is again thermal equilibrium the energy actually absorbed on A_1 must equal the energy emitted by A_1. The energy emitted by A_2 is $A_2\sigma T^4$ and this is also the radiosity of A_2 since nothing is reflected by A_2. Of this, only $FA_2\sigma T^4$ will fall on A_1 and only $\alpha FA_2\sigma T^4$ will be absorbed. A_1 will itself emit $\varepsilon A_1\sigma T^4$ and this must equal the energy absorbed.

$$\therefore \quad \varepsilon A_1\sigma T^4 = \alpha FA_2\sigma T^4$$

But

$$FA_2 = A_1 \quad \text{from (14.8)}$$

Therefore

$$\varepsilon = \alpha \tag{14.9}$$

Thus, Kirchhoff's law, as stated by equation (14.9), says that the absorptivity is equal to the emissivity at any given temperature. It follows that for a black body for which $\alpha = 1$, that $\varepsilon = 1$ and, consequently, $\varepsilon < 1$ for a grey body. Since it is possible to use a suitable value of ε for grey bodies over a temperature range, the value of α over that range is the same. This does not hold for real materials that are true selective emitters when the temperature difference is very large, because the bulk of the energy absorbed by either body is in a very different wave-length region than the energy emitted by that body.

14.5. Intensity of Radiation

The radiation from a unit area of black body is $q_b = \sigma T^4$. This radiation fans out into space, and if a small flat area is chosen the entire emittance Q_b must pass through a hemispherical surface surrounding the emitting area. It is necessary to consider the distribution of radiant energy per unit area over the spherical surface, before calculations can be made of radiation exchanges.

The intensity of radiation, I, is defined as the radiation emitted per unit time and unit solid angle subtended at the source, and per unit area of emitting surface normal to the mean direction in space, and may be expressed as

$$I = \frac{dQ_b}{(dA_2/r^2)\,dA_1\cos\phi} \tag{14.10}$$

This is shown in Fig. 14.5. dA_2/r^2 is the solid angle subtended by dA_2. dQ_b/dA_2 is the radiant energy per unit area at the hemispherical surface. If the surface can be regarded as diffuse, i.e., not mirror-like, then Lambert's law[3] states that I is constant in the hemispherical space above dA_1. From the above definition of I it thus

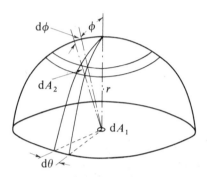

Fig. 14.5. To evaluate intensity of radiation.

follows that dQ_b/dA_2 will have a maximum value at any given r when $\phi = 0$, i.e., when dA_2 is on the normal to dA_1. Further, dQ_b/dA_2 is zero when $\phi = 90°$ and, in addition, dQ_b/dA_2 will vary inversely as r^2. In general,

$$\left(\frac{dQ_b}{dA_2}\right)_\phi = \left(\frac{dQ_b}{dA_2}\right)_n \cos\phi$$

where the suffix n implies on the normal to dA_1.

It is necessary to know the relationship between I and the total emittance from a surface. From equation (14.10),

$$dQ_b = I\left(\frac{dA_2}{r^2}\right) dA_1 \cos\phi \qquad (14.11)$$

and from Fig. 14.6 it is seen that $dA_2 = r\, d\phi\, (r \sin\phi\, d\theta) = r^2 \sin\phi\, d\phi\, d\theta$. Hence

$$dQ_b = I\, dA_1 \sin\phi \cos\phi\, d\phi\, d\theta$$

The total radiation passing through the hemispherical surface is

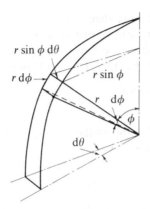

Fig. 14.6.   Detail from Fig. 14.5.

then

$$Q_b = I \, dA_1 \int_{\phi=0}^{\phi=\pi/2} \int_{\theta=0}^{\theta=2\pi} \sin\phi \cos\phi \, d\phi \, d\theta$$

$$= 2\pi I \, dA_1 \int_{\phi=0}^{\phi=\pi/2} \sin\phi \cos\phi \, d\phi$$

$$= \pi I \, dA_1$$

$$\therefore \quad I = \frac{q_b}{\pi} = \frac{\sigma T^4}{\pi} \tag{14.12}$$

14.6. Radiation Exchange between Black Surfaces

It is now possible to consider the radiation exchange between two arbitrarily disposed black surfaces of area A_1 and A_2, and at temperatures T_1 and T_2. Small elements of each surface dA_1 and dA_2 are considered as shown in Fig. 14.7. They are distance r

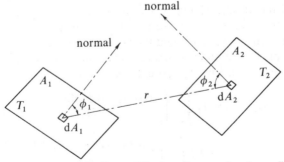

Fig. 14.7.   Arbitrarily disposed black surfaces exchanging radiation.

apart, and the line joining their centres makes angles ϕ_1 and ϕ_2 to their normals. Each element of area subtends a solid angle at the centre of the other; these are $d\omega_1$ subtended at dA_1 by dA_2, and $d\omega_2$ subtended at dA_2 by dA_1. The solid angles are given by:

$$d\omega_1 = \frac{dA_2 \cos \phi_2}{r^2}, \quad \text{and} \quad d\omega_2 = \frac{dA_1 \cos \phi_1}{r^2}$$

From equation (14.11) the radiant energy emitted by dA_1 that impinges on dA_2 is given by:

$$dQ_{b(1-2)} = I_1 \, dA_1 \cos \phi_1 \left(\frac{dA_2 \cos \phi_2}{r^2} \right) \tag{14.13}$$

Since both surfaces are black this energy is absorbed by dA_2. A similar quantity of energy is also radiated by dA_2 and absorbed by dA_1 expressed as

$$dQ_{b(2-1)} = I_2 \, dA_2 \cos \phi_2 \left(\frac{dA_1 \cos \phi_1}{r^2} \right) \tag{14.14}$$

The net exchange is

$$dQ_{b(1-2)} - dQ_{b(2-1)} = dQ_{b(12)}$$

and

$$dQ_{b(12)} = \frac{dA_1 \, dA_2 \cos \phi_1 \cos \phi_2}{r^2}(I_1 - I_2)$$

Equation (14.12) is now used to give the final result

$$dQ_{b(12)} = \frac{\sigma dA_1 \, dA_2 \cos \phi_1 \cos \phi_2}{\pi r^2}(T_1^4 - T_2^4) \tag{14.15}$$

The total radiation exchange between the two surfaces A_1 and A_2 amounts to a summation of the net energy exchange between dA_1 and all elements of area A_2, and the net exchange between all other elements of A_1 and all elements of A_2. From equation (14.13), the total energy radiated by A_1 that falls on A_2 is given by

$$Q_{b(1-2)} = I_1 \int_{A_1} \int_{A_2} \frac{\cos \phi_1 \cos \phi_2 \, dA_1 \, dA_2}{r^2}$$

$$= \sigma T_1^4 \int_{A_1} \int_{A_2} \frac{\cos \phi_1 \cos \phi_2 \, dA_1 \, dA_2}{\pi r^2}$$

But the total energy radiated by A_1 is

$$Q_{b(1)} = A_1 \sigma T_1^4$$

Hence the fraction of energy radiated by A_1 that falls on A_2 is

$$\frac{Q_{b(1-2)}}{Q_{b(1)}} = \frac{1}{A_1} \int_{A_1} \int_{A_2} \frac{\cos \phi_1 \cos \phi_2 \, dA_1 \, dA_2}{\pi r^2}$$

$$= F_{1-2} \qquad (14.16)$$

F_{1-2} is known as the geometric configuration factor of A_1 with respect to A_2. Thus the energy radiated by A_1 that falls on A_2 may be expressed as

$$Q_{b(1-2)} = F_{1-2} A_1 \sigma T_1^4 \qquad (14.17)$$

Similarly, from equation (14.14) the total energy radiated by A_2 that falls on A_1 is given by

$$Q_{b(2-1)} = \sigma T_2^4 \int_{A_1} \int_{A_2} \frac{\cos \phi_1 \cos \phi_2 \, dA_1 \, dA_2}{\pi r^2}$$

and the total energy radiated by A_2 is $A_2 \sigma T_2^4$, so that

$$\frac{Q_{b(2-1)}}{Q_{b(2)}} = \frac{1}{A_2} \int_{A_1} \int_{A_2} \frac{\cos \phi_1 \cos \phi_2 \, dA_1 \, dA_2}{\pi r^2}$$

$$= F_{2-1} \qquad (14.18)$$

and

$$Q_{b(2-1)} = F_{2-1} A_2 \sigma T_2^4 \qquad (14.19)$$

From equations (14.16) and (14.18) it is seen that F_{1-2} and F_{2-1} are simply related:

$$A_1 F_{1-2} = A_2 F_{2-1} \qquad (14.20)$$

The net radiation exchange from equations (14.17) and (14.19) can be expressed in terms of either configuration factor, thus

$$Q_{b(12)} = F_{1-2} A_1 \sigma (T_1^4 - T_2^4)$$

$$= F_{2-1} A_2 \sigma (T_1^4 - T_2^4) \qquad (14.21)$$

It is necessary to know or to be able to calculate configuration factors before black-body radiation exchanges can be determined. Only a few results will be considered here, and the reader is referred elsewhere for further information on this subject.[1,4,5]

14.6.1. Examples of the Black-Body Geometric Configuration Factor

(i) *Cases where $F_{1-2} = 1$.* The simplest case is when surface A_1 is entirely convex and is completely enclosed by A_2. Then F_{1-2} must be 1, since all the energy radiated by A_1 must fall on A_2. It follows also that F_{2-1} is A_1/A_2. In this case, the net black-body radiation exchange is

$$Q_{b(12)} = A_1\sigma(T_1^4 - T_2^4) \tag{14.22}$$

Another simple example is when surfaces A_1 and A_2 are parallel and large, and radiation occurs across the gap between them, so that in this case $A_1 = A_2$ and all radiation emitted by one falls on the other if edge effects are neglected. Hence,

$$F_{1-2} = F_{2-1} = 1$$

Concentric surfaces may be included if the gap between them is small so that little error is introduced by the small difference between the area of A_1 and A_2. The net radiation exchange is again given by equation (14.22).

(ii) *Small arbitrarily disposed areas.* In some circumstances it is possible to use equation (14.15) as it stands, if the areas dA_1 and dA_2 are small. Thus the energy received by a small disc placed in front of a small window in a furnace could be approximately calculated this way.

(iii) *Thermocouple in a circular duct.* A simple practical example of the geometric configuration factor is found in consideration of a thermocouple in a circular duct. It may be assumed that the thermocouple joint is represented by a small sphere and, further, that it is situated at the centre of a duct of length $2L$ and radius R. It is illustrated in Fig. 14.8. The line joining elements of area always

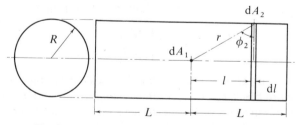

Fig. 14.8. The thermocouple configuration factor.

strikes the thermocouple joint normally, so $\cos \phi_1$ is always 1. The element of area of the duct wall is $2\pi R \, dl$. Since A_1 is a very small sphere of radius r_c, dA_1 is the disc area πr_c^2, and is constant.

Applying equation (14.16) gives

$$\frac{Q_{b(1-2)}}{Q_{b(1)}} = \frac{dA_1}{A_1} \int_{A_2} \frac{\cos \phi_2 \, 2\pi R \, dl}{\pi r^2}$$

But $\cos \phi_2 = R/r$ and $r = (R^2 + l^2)^{\frac{1}{2}}$

$$\therefore \quad \frac{Q_{b(1-2)}}{Q_{b(1)}} = \frac{\pi r_c^2}{4\pi r_c^2} \int_{-L}^{+L} \frac{2R^2 \, dl}{(R^2 + l^2)^{\frac{3}{2}}}$$

$$= \frac{1}{4}\left[\frac{2l}{(R^2 + l^2)^{\frac{1}{2}}}\right]_{-L}^{+L} = \frac{L}{(R^2 + L^2)^{\frac{1}{2}}} \quad (14.23)$$

EXAMPLE 14.1

A thermocouple situated at the centre of a circular duct 10 cm diameter by 0·25 m long has a spherical bead 2 mm diameter. It reads 185°C with gas at 200°C flowing along the duct; the wall of the duct is at 140°C. Determine a convection coefficient for heat transfer between the gas and the bead, assuming radiating surfaces are black.

Solution. Convection to the thermocouple from the gas is equal to the radiation exchange between the thermocouple and the wall. The configuration factor is $\dfrac{0\cdot125}{(0\cdot05^2 + 0\cdot125^2)^{\frac{1}{2}}} = 0\cdot93$. If h is the convection coefficient, and A the area of the bead, then

$$Q_b = 0\cdot93 \times A \times 5\cdot663\left[\left(\frac{458}{100}\right)^4 - \left(\frac{413}{100}\right)^4\right] = hA\theta$$

where $\theta = 200 - 185 = 15$

$$\therefore \quad 5\cdot26(441 - 292) = 15 \, h$$

$$\therefore \quad h = 52\cdot2 \text{ J/m}^2 \text{ s deg C}$$

(iv) Parallel and perpendicular rectangles. Radiation exchanges between finite parallel rectangles and perpendicular rectangles with a common edge occur in furnaces, etc., and details of the application of equation (14.16) to these cases may be found in ref. 5.

Calculated values of the configuration factor are available in graphical form, shown in Fig. 14.9 for parallel rectangles and Fig. 14.10 for perpendicular rectangles.

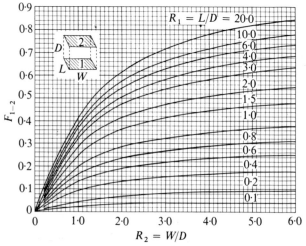

Fig. 14.9. *Configuration factors for parallel opposed rectangles. (From A. J. Chapman, Heat Transfer, The Macmillan Company, New York (1960). By permission of the publishers.)*

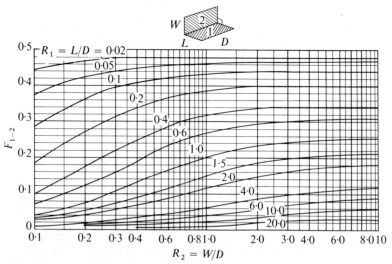

Fig. 14.10. *Configuration factor for perpendicular rectangles with a common edge. (From A. J. Chapman, Heat Transfer, The Macmillan Company, New York (1960). By permission of the publishers.)*

14.7. Grey-Body Radiation Exchanges

When radiating surfaces are grey, the emissivities of those surfaces must be taken into account as well as their geometric configuration. To enable the equation for a net energy exchange to be written in a similar manner to that for black-body radiation, Hottel[7] introduced a new factor $\mathscr{F}$. Thus a net exchange is expressed as

$$Q_{(12)} = A_1 \mathscr{F}_{1-2} \sigma (T_1^4 - T_2^4) \tag{14.24}$$

The derivation of $\mathscr{F}$ will be considered by means of an electrical analogy of radiation.[6] In the case of a net black-body radiation exchange, (14.21) is compared with Ohm's law, so that

$$Q_{b(12)} = F_{1-2} A_1 \sigma (T_1^4 - T_2^4) \quad \text{is equivalent to} \quad I = \Delta V / R$$

Hence

$$Q_{b(12)} \equiv I; \quad \sigma(T_1^4 - T_2^4) \equiv \Delta V; \quad \text{and} \quad \frac{1}{F_{1-2}A_1} \equiv R$$

The corresponding electric circuit is shown in Fig. 14.11.

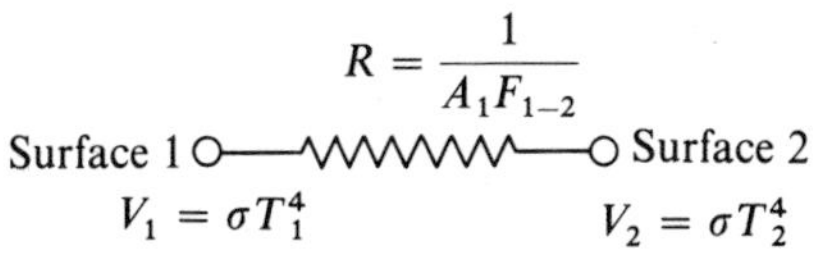

$$R = \frac{1}{A_1 F_{1-2}}$$

Surface 1 ○——WWWWW——○ Surface 2

$$V_1 = \sigma T_1^4 \qquad\qquad V_2 = \sigma T_2^4$$

Fig. 14.11. An equivalent electric circuit for a net black-body radiation exchange $Q_{b(12)} = A_1 F_{1-2} \sigma (T_1^4 - T_2^4)$.

An important initial assumption is that each radiating surface has a constant value of ρ and ε over the whole surface. From the definitions of radiosity and irradiation in section 14.2 it follows that the net rate at which energy leaves a grey surface is the difference $J - G$, and from equation (14.3)

$$J = \varepsilon Q_b + \rho G$$

$$\therefore \quad J - G = J - \frac{J - \varepsilon Q_b}{\rho}$$

and since $\rho + \varepsilon = 1$ for opaque surfaces, this reduces to

$$J - G = \frac{\varepsilon}{\rho}(Q_b - J)$$

If two surfaces only are involved, and these form an enclosure, this is also the net energy exchange between them, $Q_{(12)}$, and the equation may be compared with Ohm's law so that Q_b/A, which is σT^4, and J/A are potentials and $\rho/A\varepsilon$ is the resistance. The corresponding circuit element for either surface is shown in Fig. 14.12.

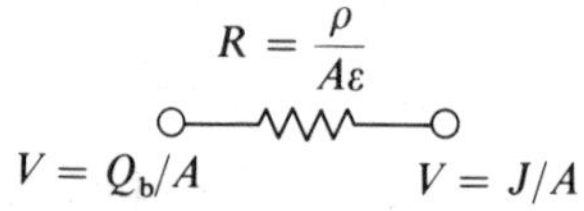

$$R = \frac{\rho}{A\varepsilon}$$

$$V = Q_b/A \qquad\qquad V = J/A$$

Fig. 14.12.

Further, for surfaces of area A_1 and A_2 (at temperatures T_1 and T_2) which have configuration factors of F_{1-2} and F_{2-1}, the net energy exchange is also the difference between the total radiation leaving A_1 which reaches A_2, and the total radiation leaving A_2 which reaches A_1. Thus

$$Q_{(12)} = \left(\frac{J_1}{A_1}\right)A_1 F_{1-2} - \left(\frac{J_2}{A_2}\right)A_2 F_{2-1}$$

But, from the reciprocal relationship, $A_1 F_{1-2} = A_2 F_{2-1}$,

$$\therefore \qquad Q_{(12)} = \left(\frac{J_1}{A_1} - \frac{J_2}{A_2}\right)A_1 F_{1-2}$$

This may also be represented by a circuit element, with potentials J_1/A_1 and J_2/A_2 and resistance $1/A_1 F_{1-2}$, as shown in Fig. 14.13.

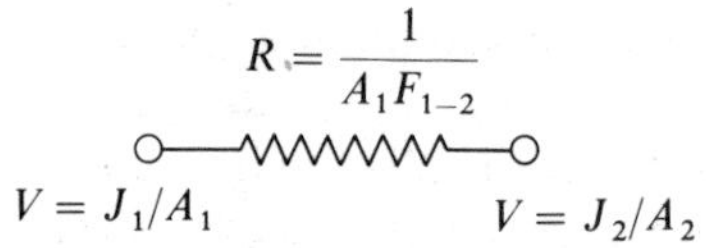

$$R = \frac{1}{A_1 F_{1-2}}$$

$$V = J_1/A_1 \qquad\qquad V = J_2/A_2$$

Fig. 14.13.

To simulate completely an energy exchange between the surfaces A_1 and A_2, three circuit elements may be joined in series as shown in Fig. 14.14, the whole circuit now being compared to equation (14.24). σT_1^4 and σT_2^4 are the end potentials (equivalent to $Q_{b(1)}/A_1$ and $Q_{b(2)}/A_2$), and the total resistance is

$$\frac{\rho_1}{A_1 \varepsilon_1} + \frac{1}{A_1 F_{1-2}} + \frac{\rho_2}{A_2 \varepsilon_2}$$

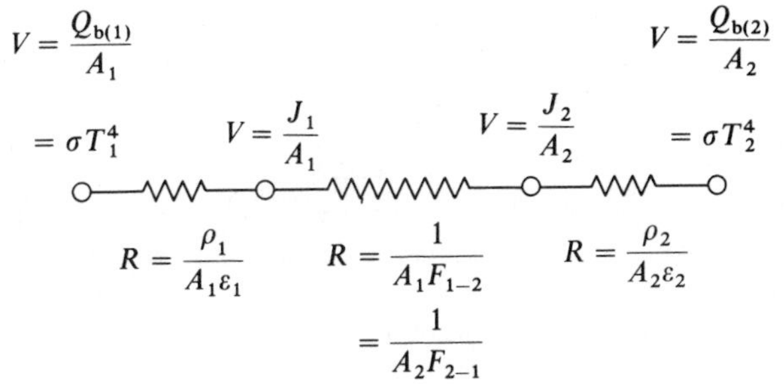

$$V = \frac{Q_{b(1)}}{A_1} \qquad\qquad\qquad V = \frac{Q_{b(2)}}{A_2}$$

$$= \sigma T_1^4 \qquad V = \frac{J_1}{A_1} \qquad V = \frac{J_2}{A_2} \qquad = \sigma T_2^4$$

$$R = \frac{\rho_1}{A_1 \varepsilon_1} \qquad R = \frac{1}{A_1 F_{1-2}} \qquad R = \frac{\rho_2}{A_2 \varepsilon_2}$$

$$= \frac{1}{A_2 F_{2-1}}$$

Fig. 14.14.   Complete circuit for radiation exchange between two grey surfaces forming an enclosure.

From equation (14.24) the resistance is also given by $1/A_1 \mathscr{F}_{1-2}$, hence

$$\frac{1}{A_1 \mathscr{F}_{1-2}} = \frac{\rho_1}{A_1 \varepsilon_1} + \frac{1}{A_1 F_{1-2}} + \frac{\rho_2}{A_2 \varepsilon_2}$$

Multiplying both sides by A_1 and substituting $1 - \varepsilon$ for ρ gives

$$\frac{1}{\mathscr{F}_{1-2}} = \left(\frac{1-\varepsilon_1}{\varepsilon_1}\right) + \frac{1}{F_{1-2}} + \frac{A_1}{A_2}\left(\frac{1-\varepsilon_2}{\varepsilon_2}\right)$$

$$\therefore \quad \mathscr{F}_{1-2} = \frac{1}{\left(\dfrac{1}{\varepsilon_1} - 1\right) + \dfrac{1}{F_{1-2}} + \dfrac{A_1}{A_2}\left(\dfrac{1}{\varepsilon_2} - 1\right)} \qquad (14.25)$$

This result may be used for any two surfaces of area A_1 and A_2, provided they form an enclosure, for which the configuration factor is F_{1-2}. Equation (14.25) simplifies for the special case of infinite parallel or concentric grey planes for which $F_{1-2} = 1$ and $A_1 = A_2$. Then,

$$\mathscr{F}_{1-2} = \frac{1}{\dfrac{1}{\varepsilon_1} + \dfrac{1}{\varepsilon_2} - 1} \qquad (14.26)$$

This result can also be readily achieved without reference to the equivalent electric circuit.

A further simple result which is useful is that if A_1 is completely enclosed by A_2, so that $F_{1-2} = 1$, and A_2 is large compared with A_1 so that

$$\frac{A_1}{A_2}\left(\frac{1}{\varepsilon_2} - 1\right) \approx 0$$

then equation (14.25) reduces to

$$\mathcal{F}_{1-2} = \varepsilon_1 \qquad (14.27)$$

EXAMPLE 14.2

A small oven measures 0·4 m by 0·5 m by 0·3 m high. The floor of the oven receives radiation from all the walls and roof which are at 300°C and have an emissivity of 0·8. The floor is maintained at 150°C and has an emissivity of 0·6. Calculate the radiation exchange.

Solution. A_1 is the total area of walls and roof, which is 0·74 m². A_2 is the area of the floor, 0·2 m². Since A_1 encloses A_2, $F_{2-1} = 1$ and $F_{1-2} = A_2/A_1 = 0·27$.

The grey-body factor $\mathcal{F}_{1-2}$ is
$$\cfrac{1}{\left(\cfrac{1}{0·8} - 1\right) + \cfrac{1}{0·27} + 3·7\left(\cfrac{1}{0·6} - 1\right)}$$
$$= 0·156$$

The radiation exchange is $0·156 \times 0·74 \times 5·663\left[\left(\dfrac{573}{100}\right)^4 - \left(\dfrac{423}{100}\right)^4\right]$
$$= 495 \text{ watts}$$

14.8. Radiation Coefficients

Radiation coefficients were mentioned in chapter 3 when describing heat transfer at surfaces with a view to determining an overall heat transfer coefficient. A radiation coefficient can be deduced simply by comparing the equation $Q = Ah_R(T_1 - T_2)$ with the expression for the radiation exchange. Thus, if the radiation exchange is

$$Q_{b(12)} = \sigma A_1 F_{1-2}(T_1^4 - T_2^4)$$
$$= A_1 h_R(T_1 - T_2)$$

it follows that

$$h_R = \frac{\sigma F_{1-2}(T_1^4 - T_2^4)}{(T_1 - T_2)}$$
$$= \sigma F_{1-2}(T_1 + T_2)(T_1^2 + T_2^2) \qquad (14.28)$$

Clearly $\mathcal{F}_{1-2}$ may be substituted for F_{1-2} depending on the circumstances.

EXAMPLE 14.3

A coke stove of surface area $10\,\text{ft}^2$, emissivity 0.8 and surface temperature $300°F$ is enclosed in a large room with uniform grey surfaces at $65°F$. Determine the radiation coefficient, and the radiation heat transfer.

Solution. Equation (14.24) may be used to calculate the heat transfer, with $\mathscr{F}_{1-2} = \varepsilon_1$ from (14.27), since the room is large. Hence equation (14.28) for this case will be

$$h_R = \sigma\varepsilon(T_1 + T_2)(T_1^2 + T_2^2)$$

Hence

$$h_R = 0.171 \times 10^{-8} \times 0.8(760 + 525)(760^2 + 525^2)$$

$$= 1.500\ \text{Btu/ft}^2\ \text{h deg R}$$

and,

$$Q_{(12)} = 0.8 \times 0.171 \times 10\left[\left(\frac{760}{100}\right)^4 - \left(\frac{525}{100}\right)^4\right]$$

$$= 3530\ \text{Btu/h.}\ (\text{Also}\ Q_{(12)} = 1.5 \times 10 \times 235 = 3530\ \text{Btu/h})$$

PROBLEMS

1. Derive an expression for the rate of heat transfer by radiation between two parallel surfaces of equal area A, separated by a small distance. The respective absolute temperatures of the two surfaces are T_1 and T_2 whilst the emissivities are ε_1 and ε_2. The Stefan–Boltzmann constant is σ.

A double walled vessel contains an equilibrium mixture of ice and water at atmospheric pressure. The space between the two walls is evacuated and the surfaces enclosing it are covered with a layer of silver of emissivity 0.02. The temperature of the surface adjoining the ice–water mixture is $32°F$ and that of the opposite surface is $70°F$. Assuming that the two walls are separated by a small, uniform, distance and each has an area of $1\,\text{ft}^2$, calculate the rate of melting of ice in the mixture when heat transfer between the mixture and the surroundings by conduction and convection can be neglected. Take the enthalpy of fusion of ice to be $143\ \text{Btu/lb}$. (Ans. $0.059\ \text{lb/day.}$) (*Queen Mary College, London*).

2. A spherical thermocouple is situated at the middle of the length and on the axis of a pipe of length L and diameter D to measure the temperature of the gas flowing through the pipe. Assuming that the couple is so small in comparison with the duct that the surface of the couple is always perpendicular to the direction of radiation, deduce from first principles the expression

$$F_{h-c} = \frac{L}{\sqrt{(D^2 + L^2)}}$$

which gives the 'area factor' of the system. Both the couple and the pipe may be considered to be black bodies.

In an installation similar to that described above, the thermocouple is $\frac{1}{8}$ in. in diameter and the pipe is 3 ft long and 1 ft in diameter. The gas temperature is 300°F and the internal surface of the pipe is 150°F. Heat is being transferred from the gas to the couple at the rate of 250 Btu/h ft². What would be the reading of the thermocouple if both the couple and the pipe can be considered as black? The expression for the area factor given above may be used. (Ans. 276°F.) (*King's College, London*).

3. A thermocouple situated in the passage of an air pre-heater may be considered to be a sphere of 1.9 mm diameter and of emissivity 0.56. The passage may be regarded as a black spherical enclosure.

The air flows along the passage at 2.44 m/s, and the heat transfer by convection between the air and the spherical thermocouple element is given by $Hd/k = 0.4Re^{0.65}$, with the diameter of the sphere as the characteristic dimension.

A galvanometer connected to this thermocouple indicates a temperature of 316°C whilst that connected to a thermocouple embedded in the wall of the duct indicates a temperature of 455°C. Calculate the true temperature of the air. (Ans. 288°C.) (*King's College, London*).

4. A galvanized steel pipe of outside diameter 7.62 cm passes through a large enclosure containing air in which the walls are at 26.7°C. The surface coefficient of heat transfer by convection to the air is 8.52 J/m² s deg C. The pipe surface has an emissivity of 0.28 and a constant temperature of 99°C. Determine the apparent coefficient of heat transfer due to radiation.

It is proposed to cover the pipe with a layer of asbestos felt, 0.159 cm thick. Assuming as a first approximation that the apparent radiation coefficient is independent of temperature, and that the temperature of the pipe remains constant, estimate the equilibrium temperature of the outer surface of the asbestos and compare the rates of heat transfer from the pipe with and without insulation. Comment on the result in the light of the assumptions made.

For asbestos, conductivity is 0.0865 J/m s deg C, emissivity is 0.93. (Ans. 2.43 J/m² s deg C, 68.8°C, 228 and 188 J/m s.) (*University of London*).

5. A horizontal pipe of 3 in. outer diameter is thermally insulated by means of a composite lagging consisting of an inner layer 1 in. thick, and an outer layer 2 in. thick. The coefficients of thermal conductivity are 0.072 and 0.38 Btu/ft h deg F respectively. The outer surface temperature is 120°F when the temperature of the surroundings is 60°F. Estimate the temperatures at the inner and outer surfaces of the inner layer of lagging. Assume that the coefficient of convective heat transfer is given by $h = 0.22[(t_s - t_a)/d]^{0.25}$ Btu/ft² h deg F where t_s is the outer surface temperature, t_a is the temperature of the surroundings and d ft is the outer surface diameter. The emissivity factor for the outer surface is 0.15 and the view factor is unity. (Ans. 281°F, 149°F.) (*University of Glasgow*).

6. An air heater consists of a cylindrical former 0·508 m long and 1·9 cm diameter closely wound with thin resistance wire. The heater is installed across a rectangular duct 0·508 m wide by 0·127 m across, into which air is blown at a speed of 7·15 m/s at 15·6°C and 101·3 kN/m². The wire surface temperature is maintained at 550°C and its emissivity is 0·85. The duct walls, at 15·6°C may be assumed black to incident radiant heat. Convective transfer is correlated by

$$\frac{hd}{k} = 0.26\left(\frac{\rho U d}{\mu}\right)^{0.6}\left(\frac{\mu c_p}{k}\right)^{0.3}$$

where U is the cold entry velocity. Estimate the kilowatt input to the heater. Predict the effect of varying former diameter d by establishing an expression for air temperature rise in terms of d. (Ans. 1·72 kW.) (*University of Glasgow*).

7. Using the concepts of 'radiosity' and 'irradiation', derive an expression for the radiant heat transfer between a grey body and a grey enclosing surface.

A spherical liquid oxygen tank 1 ft diameter is enclosed concentrically in a spherical container 1 ft 4 in. diameter and the space between is evacuated. The tank surface is at $-298°F$ and has emissivity 0·2. The container surface is at 60°F and has emissivity 0·25. Determine the net radiant heat transfer rate.

If a concentric spherical shield 1 ft 2 in. diameter, emissivity 0·07 is added, determine the equilibrium temperature of the shield and the new heat transfer rate. (Ans. 58·2 Btu/h, $-12°F$, 14·4 Btu/h.) (*University of Manchester*).

8. Using the conventional notation, show that

$$\dot{Q} = \frac{E_1 E_2 \sigma}{E_2 + E_1(1 - E_2)}(T_1^4 - T_2^4)$$

for the rate of radiant heat exchange between a pair of large, parallel, thermally grey plates.

Calculate the rate of exchange of energy for such a case when the temperatures are 1040°F and 540°F. The emissivities of the surfaces are 0·85 and 0·75. (Ans. 15,300 Btu/ft² h.) (*University of Manchester*).

9. Distinguish briefly between the various factors commonly used to modify the simple Stefan–Boltzmann relation for transfer of heat by radiation.

A furnace consists essentially of a long refractory tube, cross-section rectangular 0·305 m by 0·203 m. The furnace encloses a heat-resisting steel pipe of 7·62 cm o.d. The furnace wall temperature is maintained at 872°C, the pipe surface at 371°C. Assuming both surfaces to be grey, calculate the net rate of heat transfer by radiation.

Emissivity of furnace wall = 0·8 ; emissivity of steel = 0·40.

In the usual nomenclature :

$$1/\mathscr{F}_{12} = 1/F_{12} + (1/\varepsilon_1 - 1) + (A_1/A_2)(1/\varepsilon_2 - 1)$$

(Ans. 8260 J/m s.) (*University of Leeds*).

10. The interior of a billet reheating furnace is 40 ft long with rectangular cross-section 10 ft by 3 ft. Billets are conveyed transversely through the furnace at a slow rate, entering at 400°F and leaving at 1200°F. Billet and conveyor gear may be regarded as a bar 8 ft long by 9 in. square. Heating is radiant only, the furnace walls being maintained at a uniform temperature of 1600°F. Emissivity of walls is 0·9, of billet 0·8. Given there are no re-radiating partitions, make further suitable assumptions and estimate the inlet and exit values of the furnace heat load.

$$\frac{1}{\mathscr{F}_{12}} = \frac{1}{F_{12}} + \left(\frac{1}{\varepsilon_1} - 1\right) + \frac{A_1}{A_2}\left(\frac{1}{\varepsilon_2} - 1\right)$$

(Ans. 600,000 and 357,000 Btu/h.) (*University of Leeds*).

11. A molten metal bath is heated in a furnace by hot gases which pass between the surface of the metal and a suspended brick roof. The hot gases which may be considered non-radiating are at 1370°C and the brick roof is at 1094°C. There is no heat loss through the furnace roof, all heat reaching it being radiated to the metal surface. Convective heat transfer coefficients are: from gas to roof, 28·4 J/m² s deg C, gas to molten metal, 39·8 J/m² s deg C. From the radiation viewpoint the roof and metal surface are of equal area and may be regarded as infinite parallel planes. The roof may be taken as black, and the metal surface as grey, emissivity 0·2.

Calculate the total rate of heat transfer to the molten metal per square metre of surface. (Ans. 21,870 J/m² s.) (*University of Leeds*).

REFERENCES

1. Jakob, M. *Heat Transfer*, Vol. 1, John Wiley and Sons, Inc., New York (1949).
2. Kirchhoff, G. *Ostwalds Klassiker d. exakten Wissens.*, 100, Leipzig (1898).
3. Lambert, J. H. *Photometria* (1860).
4. McAdams, W. H. *Heat Transmission* (Chapter 4, Hottel, H. C.), 3rd ed., McGraw-Hill Book Company, Inc., New York (1954).
5. Chapman, A. J. *Heat Transfer*, The Macmillan Company, New York (1960).
6. Oppenheim, A. K. *Amer. Soc. Mech. Engs*, Paper 54-A75 (1954).
7. Hottel, H. C. *Notes on Radiant Heat Transmission*, Chem. Eng. Dept., M.I.T. (1951).

Appendix
Units, and conversion factors
Tables of property values

This book appears at a time when a move to adopt the metric system of units is in progress. This means that both student and practising engineer are faced with a period when familiarity with both metric and British units is required.

The bulk of heat transfer literature in the English speaking world is in the British system of units. Continental practice is to use metric units, either the metre, kilogramme, second, (m.k.s.), system or alternatively, the centimetre, gramme, second, (c.g.s.), system. As a rationalized set of metric units is now coming into use, called the Système International d'Unités, (SI), only these and British units are used in this book.

Since in British engineering practice the mixed units of pound force, lbf, and pound mass, lb, are frequently used, it is necessary to establish clearly their relationship. In mechanics, Newton's second law of motion may be expressed as

$$\text{force} = \frac{\text{mass} \times \text{acceleration}}{\text{a constant}}$$

The constant has no dimensions and is numerically one in consistent or absolute systems of units. It is given the symbol g_0 or g_c. In the force, length, time system of basic units the units used are the pound force, the foot, and the second. These units are consistent and the derived unit of mass is the slug, given by

$$1 \text{ slug} = \frac{1 \text{ lbf s}^2}{\text{ft}}$$

Another system of basic units is the pound mass, foot, second system, in which force is the derived unit. These units are also consistent, with the unit of force being

$$1 \text{ poundal} = \frac{1 \text{ lb ft}}{s^2}$$

In the commonly used mixed system of units, the pound force, pound mass, foot and second are all basic units. They are not consistent, so that

$$1 \text{ lbf} = \frac{1 \text{ lb} \times 32 \cdot 174 \text{ ft/s}^2}{g_0}$$

since the pound force is defined as the force necessary to give one pound mass an acceleration of $32 \cdot 174 \text{ ft/s}^2$, which is the standard gravitational acceleration at sea level. In these units it follows that

$$g_0 = 32 \cdot 174 \frac{\text{lb ft}}{\text{lbf s}^2} = 32 \cdot 174 \frac{\text{poundal}}{\text{lbf}}$$

Thus g_0 is a number relating the poundal and the pound force. Putting 1 lbf as $32 \cdot 174$ lb ft/s^2 in the slug–lbf relationship above yields the fact that 1 slug is $32 \cdot 174$ lb.

The temperature scale of Fahrenheit is associated with British units, leading to the British Thermal Unit as the unit of heat. The British Thermal Unit, Btu, is the heat transfer which causes the temperature of 1 lb of water at atmospheric pressure to rise from 60 to 61°F. The thermodynamic temperature scale which has the same unit value as Fahrenheit is the Rankine scale. Values in the two scales are related by

$$T \text{ in } °R = t \text{ in } °F + 460$$

Sometimes the temperature scale of Centigrade is used with British units of mass, etc., and the corresponding unit of heat is the Centigrade Heat Unit, Chu. It is defined in a similar manner to the Btu. The two are related by

$$1 \text{ Btu} = \frac{5}{9} \text{ Chu}; \quad \left(\text{since } 1 \text{ deg F} = \frac{5}{9} \text{ deg C}\right)$$

The thermodynamic temperature scale having the same unit value as Centigrade is the Kelvin scale. Values are related by

$$T \text{ in } °K = t \text{ in } °C + 273$$

The unit of time commonly in use in heat transfer practice is the hour, h. This probably arose from the early association with steam power engineering, where the unit of work is the horse power hour.

Throughout this book, equations are written so that consistent units are always required. The use of g_0 is not necessary. Care must therefore be taken to ensure the correct units are used, particularly in examples of Reynolds analogy, where shear stress and heat transfer equations are compared. Thus, consider equation (7.15):

$$\frac{q_w}{\tau_w} = \frac{c_p \theta_s}{v_s}$$

Normally, q_w is in Btu/ft^2 h, τ_w is in lbf/ft^2, c_p is in Btu/lb deg F, and v_s is in ft/s. The most convenient way of achieving consistency is to express q_w in Btu/ft^2 s, and c_p in Btu/slug deg F. Correct numerical solutions would then be obtained. These difficulties would not arise with the use of rationalized units.

The SI units are based on the metre, m, the kilogramme, kg, and the second. The unit of force is the newton, N. Thus:

$$1 \text{ N} = 1 \text{ kg} \times 1 \text{ m/s}^2$$

The unit of heat or energy is the joule, J, which is the work done when the point of application of a force of one newton is displaced through a distance of one metre in the direction of the force. One joule per second is the watt, W. The Centigrade and Kelvin temperature scales are used. Referring again to equation (7.15), consistent units of all physical quantities would be used: q_w is in J/m^2 s, (or W/m^2), τ_w is in N/m^2, c_p is in J/kg deg C, and v_s is in m/s.

The physical quantities encountered in heat transfer, together with their units in SI and the British system, and conversion factors, are tabulated on page 222.

Thermal property values are tabulated on pages 223–238.

Conversion Factors

Physical quantity	British units	SI	Conversion factor*	Reciprocal conversion factor*
Basic engineering units:				
Mass	lb	kg	0·4536	2·2045
	slug	kg	14·594	0·06852
Length	ft	m	0·3048	3·2808
Force	lbf	N	4·4482	0·2248
Energy	Btu	J	1055·06	$9·4781 \times 10^{-4}$
	ft lbf	J	1·3558	0·7375
Power	550 ft lbf/s = 1 h.p.	W	745·69	$1·3410 \times 10^{-3}$
Heat transfer units:				
Q	Btu/h	J/s, or W	0·2931	3·4118
q	Btu/ft² h	J/m² s	3·155	0·3169
h, U	Btu/ft² h deg F	J/m² s deg C	5·678	0·1761
k	Btu/ft h deg F	J/m s deg C	1·731	0·5777
c_p	Btu/lb deg F	J/kg deg C	4186·8	$2·388 \times 10^{-4}$
ρ	lb/ft³	kg/m³	16·0185	0·06243
μ	lb/ft h	kg/m s, or N s/m²	$4·134 \times 10^{-4}$	$2·4189 \times 10^3$
$\nu, \alpha, \varepsilon, D$	ft²/h	m²/s	$2·581 \times 10^{-5}$	$3·8744 \times 10^4$
τ, P, p	lbf/ft²	N/m²	47·880	0·02089
τ, P, p	lbf/in²	N/m²	$6·8948 \times 10^3$	$1·4503 \times 10^{-4}$

* Multiply the numerical value in British units by the conversion factor to obtain the equivalent in SI; multiply the numerical value in SI by the reciprocal conversion factor to obtain the equivalent in British units.

Table A.1. Thermal Properties of Solids: Metals

	Properties at 20°C				k, W/m deg C				
	ρ $\left(\dfrac{kg}{m^3}\right)$	c_p $\left(\dfrac{J}{kg\,deg\,C}\right)$	k $\left(\dfrac{W}{m\,deg\,C}\right)$	α $\left(\dfrac{m^2}{s}\right)$	100	200	300 (°C)	400	600
Aluminium, pure	2707	896	204	8.42×10^{-5}	206	215	229	249	
Duralumin, 94–96 Al, 3–5 Cu	2787	883	164	6.68	182	194			
Lead	11,370	130	34.6	2.34	33.4	31.5	29.8		
Iron, pure	7897	452	72.7	2.03	67.5	62.3	55.4	48.5	39.8
Iron, wrought, C < 0.5%	7849	460	58.9	1.63	57.1	51.9	48.5	45.0	36.4
Iron, cast, C ≈ 4%	7272	419	51.9	1.70					
Carbon steel, C ≈ 0.5%	7833	465	53.7	1.47	51.9	48.5	45.0	41.5	34.6
Carbon steel, C = 1.5%	7753	486	36.4	0.97	36.3	36.3	34.6	32.9	31.2
Nickel steel, 10%	7945	460	26.0	0.72					
Nickel steel, 30%	8073	460	12.1	0.33					
Nickel steel, 50%	8266	460	13.8	0.36					
Nickel steel, 70%	8506	460	26.0	0.67					
Nickel steel, 90%	8762	460	46.7	1.16					
Chrome steel, 1%	7865	460	60.6	1.67	55.4	51.9	46.7	41.5	36.4
Chrome steel, 5%	7833	460	39.8	1.11	38.1	36.4	36.4	32.9	29.4
Chrome steel, 10%	7785	460	31.2	0.87	31.2	31.2	29.4	29.4	31.2
Cr–Ni steel, 18% Cr, 8% Ni	7817	460	16.3	0.44	17.3	17.3	19.0	19.0	22.5
Ni–Cr steel, 20% Ni, 15% Cr	7865	460	14.0	0.39	15.1	15.1	16.3	17.3	19.0
Manganese steel, 2%	7865	460	38.1	1.05	36.4	36.4	36.4	34.6	32.9

Table A.1. *Continued*

	ρ $\left(\dfrac{kg}{m^3}\right)$	c_p $\left(\dfrac{J}{kg\ deg\ C}\right)$	k $\left(\dfrac{W}{m\ deg\ C}\right)$	α $\left(\dfrac{m^2}{s}\right)$	100	200	300 (°C)	400	600
		Properties at 20°C					k, W/m deg C		
Tungsten steel, 2%	7961	444	62·3	$1·76 \times 10^{-5}$	58·9	53·7	48·5	45·0	36·4
Silicon steel, 2%	7673	460	31·2	0·89					
Copper, pure	8954	383	386	11·2	379	374	369	364	353
Bronze, 75 Cu, 25 Sn	8660	343	26·0	0·86					
Brass, 70 Cu, 30 Zn	8522	385	111	3·41	128	144	147	147	
German silver, 62 Cu 15 Ni, 22 Zn	8618	394	24·9	0·73	31·2	39·8	45·0	48·5	
Constantan, 60 Cu, 40 Ni	8922	410	22·7	0·61	22·2	26·0			
Magnesium, pure	1746	1013	171	9·71	168	163	158		
Molybdenum	10,220	251	123	4·79	118	114	111	109	106
Nickel, 99·9% pure	8906	446	90·0	2·27	83·1	72·7	64·0	58·9	
Silver, 99·9% pure	10,520	234	407	16·6	415	374	362	360	
Tungsten	19,350	134	163	6·27	151	142	133	126	113
Zinc, pure	7144	384	112	4·11	109	106	100	93·5	
Tin, pure	7304	227	64·0	3·88	58·9	57·1			

Adapted from Table A–1, E. R. G. Eckert and R. M. Drake, Jr., *Heat and Mass Transfer*, McGraw-Hill Book Company, New York (1959).

Table A.2. Thermal Properties of Solids: non-Metals

	c_p $\left(\dfrac{J}{kg\,deg\,C}\right)$	ρ $\left(\dfrac{kg}{m^3}\right)$	t (°C)	k $\left(\dfrac{W}{m\,deg\,C}\right)$	α $\left(\dfrac{m^2}{s}\right)$
Bakelite	1590	1273	20	0·232	$0·0114 \times 10^{-5}$
Bricks:					
Common	837	1602	20	0·692	0·0516
Face		2050	20	1·32	
Chrome	837	3011	200	2·32	0·0929
			550	2·48	0·0981
			900	1·99	0·0800
Diatomaceous earth			204	0·242	
(fired)			872	0·312	
Fire clay					
(burnt 1450°C)	963	2323	500	1·28	0·0568
			800	1·37	0·0619
			1100	1·402	0·0619
Magnesite	1130		204	3·81	
			648	2·77	
			1204	1·90	
Concrete	879	1906–2307	20	0·814–1·40	0·0490–0·0697
Glass, plate	837	2707	20	0·762	0·0336
Plaster, gypsum	837	1442	21	0·485	0·0413
Stone:					
Granite	816	2643		1·73–3·98	0·0800–0·183
Limestone	908	2483	99	1·26	0·0568
			299	1·33	0·0594
Marble	808	2499–2707	20	2·77	0·0394
Sandstone	712	2163–2307	20	1·63–2·08	0·106–0·127
Wood, cross grain:					
Cypress		464	30	0·097	
Fir	2721	417	24	0·109	0·0095
Oak	2387	609–481	30	0·166	0·0126
Yellow pine	2805	641	24	0·147	0·0083
Wood, radial:					
Oak	2387	609–481	20	0·173–0·207	0·0111–0·0121
Fir	2721	417	20	0·138	0·0124

Table A.2. *Continued*

	c_p $\left(\dfrac{J}{kg\,deg\,C}\right)$	ρ $\left(\dfrac{kg}{m^3}\right)$	t $(°C)$	k $\left(\dfrac{W}{m\,deg\,C}\right)$	α $\left(\dfrac{m^2}{s}\right)$
Asbestos	816	577	0	0·151	
	816	577	100	0·192	
Cotton	1298	80·1	20	0·0589	0·194
Cork, board		160	30	0·0433	
Cork, expanded scrap	1884	44·8–	20	0·0363	0·0155–
		119			0·0439
Earth, coarse gravelly	1842	2050	20	0·519	0·0139
Felt, wool		330	30	0·0519	
Fibre, insulating board		237	21	0·0485	
Glass wool	670	200	20	0·0398	0·0284
Ice	1926	913	0	2·22	0·124
Silk	1382	57·7	20	0·0363	0·0439

Adapted from A. J. Chapman, *Heat Transfer*, The Macmillan Company, New York (1960); L. S. Marks, *Mechanical Engineers' Handbook*, 5th ed., McGraw-Hill Book Company, Inc., New York (1951); W. H. McAdams, *Heat Transmission*, 3rd ed., McGraw-Hill Book Company, Inc., New York (1954); and E. R. G. Eckert and R. M. Drake, Jr., *Heat and Mass Transfer*, McGraw-Hill Book Company, Inc., New York (1959).

Table A.3. Physical Properties of some Common Low Melting Point Metals

	Melting point (°C)	Boiling point (°C)	Temp. (°C)	ρ $\left(\dfrac{kg}{m^3}\right)$	μ $\left(\dfrac{Ns}{m^2}\right)$	c_p $\left(\dfrac{J}{kg\ deg\ C}\right)$	k $\left(\dfrac{W}{m\ deg\ C}\right)$	Pr
Bismuth	272	1480	315	10,010	1.62×10^{-3}	144	16.4	0.014
			760	9467	0.79	164	15.6	0.0084
Lead	328	1738	371	10,540	2.40	159	16.1	0.024
			704	10,140	1.37	155	14.9	0.016
Lithium	179	1318	204	506	0.59	4187	38.1	0.065
			983	442	0.42	4187		
Mercury	−39	357	10	13,570	1.59	138	8.14	0.027
			315	12,850	0.87	134	14.0	0.0084
Potassium	64	760	149	807	0.37	796	45.0	0.0066
			704	674	0.13	754	33.1	0.0031
Sodium	97	884	204	902	0.43	1340	80.3	0.0072
			704	779	0.18	1256	59.7	0.0038
Sodium–Potassium, 22% Na	19	826	93.5	849	0.49	946	24.4	0.019
			760	690	0.16	883		
Sodium–Potassium, 56% Na	−11	795	93.5	887	0.58	1130	25.6	0.026
			760	740	0.16	1042	28.9	0.058
Lead–Bismuth, 44.5% Pb	125	1670	288	10,350	1.76	147	10.7	0.024
			649	9835	1.15			

Adapted from Table 16–1, J. G. Knudsen and D. L. Katz, *Fluid Dynamics and Heat Transfer*, McGraw-Hill Book Company, Inc., New York (1958).

Table A.4.   Thermal Properties of Saturated Liquids

Water (H_2O)

t (°C)	ρ (kg/m³)	c_p (J/kg deg C)	ν (m²/s)	k (W/m deg C)	α (m²/s)	Pr	β (1/deg K)
0	1002	4218	0.179×10^{-5}	0·552	13.1×10^{-8}	13·6	
20	1001	4182	0·101	0·597	14·3	7·02	0.18×10^{-3}
40	994·6	4178	0·0658	0·628	15·1	4·34	
60	985·4	4184	0·0477	0·651	15·5	3·02	
80	974·1	4196	0·0364	0·668	16·4	2·22	
100	960·6	4216	0·0294	0·680	16·8	1·74	
120	945·3	4250	0·0247	0·685	17·1	1·446	
140	928·3	4283	0·0214	0·684	17·2	1·241	
160	909·7	4342	0·0189	0·680	17·3	1·099	
180	889·0	4417	0·0173	0·675	17·2	1·004	
200	866·7	4505	0·0160	0·665	17·1	0·937	
220	842·4	4610	0·0149	0·653	16·8	0·891	
240	815·7	4756	0·0143	0·635	16·4	0·871	
260	785·9	4949	0·0137	0·611	15·6	0·874	
280	752·5	5208	0·0135	0·580	14·8	0·910	
300	714·3	5728	0·0135	0·540	13·2	1·019	

Methyl Chloride (CH_3Cl)

			$\times 10^{-5}$		$\times 10^{-8}$	
−50	1053	1476	0·0320	0·215	13·9	2·31
−40	1033	1483	0·0318	0·209	13·7	2·32
−30	1017	1492	0·0314	0·202	13·4	2·35
−20	999·4	1504	0·0309	0·196	13·0	2·38
−10	981·4	1519	0·0306	0·187	12·6	2·43
0	962·4	1538	0·0302	0·178	12·1	2·49
10	942·4	1560	0·0297	0·171	11·7	2·55
20	923·3	1586	0·0292	0·163	11·1	2·63
30	903·1	1616	0·0287	0·154	10·6	2·72
40	883·1	1650	0·0281	0·144	9·96	2·83
50	861·2	1689	0·0274	0·133	9·21	2·97

$2·63 \times 10^{-3}$

Freon (CCl_2F_2)

			$\times 10^{-5}$		$\times 10^{-8}$	
−50	1547	875·0	0·0310	0·0675	5·01	6·2
−40	1519	884·7	0·0279	0·0692	5·13	5·4
−30	1490	895·6	0·0253	0·0710	5·26	4·8
−20	1461	907·3	0·0235	0·0727	5·39	4·4
−10	1430	920·3	0·0221	0·0727	5·50	4·0
0	1397	934·5	0·0214	0·0727	5·57	3·8
10	1364	949·6	0·0203	0·0727	5·60	3·6
20	1330	965·9	0·0198	0·0727	5·60	3·5
30	1295	983·5	0·0194	0·0710	5·60	3·5
40	1257	1002	0·0191	0·0692	5·55	3·5
50	1216	1022	0·0189	0·0675	5·44	3·5

Table A.4.   Continued

t (°C)	ρ (kg/m³)	c_p (J/kg deg C)	ν (m²/s)	k (W/m deg C)	α (m²/s)	Pr	β (1/deg K)
Glycerin (C₃H₅(OH)₃)							
0	1276	2261	$8\cdot31 \times 10^{-3}$	0·282	$9\cdot83 \times 10^{-8}$	$84\cdot7 \times 10^3$	
10	1270	2320	3·00	0·284	9·65	31·0	
20	1264	2387	1·17	0·286	9·47	12·5	$0\cdot504 \times 10^{-3}$
30	1258	2445	0·50	0·286	9·29	5·38	
40	1252	2512	0·22	0·286	9·13	2·45	
50	1245	2583	0·15	0·287	8·93	1·63	
Ethylene glycol (C₂H₄(OH)₂)							
0	1130	2294	$5\cdot75 \times 10^{-5}$	0·242	$9\cdot34 \times 10^{-8}$	615	
20	1117	2382	1·92	0·249	9·39	204	
40	1101	2474	0·869	0·256	9·39	93	$0\cdot648 \times 10^{-3}$
60	1088	2562	0·475	0·260	9·31	51	
80	1078	2650	0·298	0·261	9·21	32·4	
100	1059	2742	0·203	0·263	9·08	22·4	

Engine oil (unused)

0	899	1796	4.28×10^{-3}	0·147	9.11×10^{-8}	47,100	0.702×10^{-3}
20	888	1880	0·90	0·145	8·72	10,400	
40	876	1964	0·24	0·144	8·33	2870	
60	864	2047	0·0839	0·140	8·00	1050	
80	852	2131	0·0375	0·138	7·69	490	
100	840	2219	0·0203	0·137	7·38	276	
120	829	2307	0·0123	0·135	7·10	175	
140	817	2395	0·0080	0·133	6·86	116	
160	806	2483	0·0056	0·132	6·63	84	

Mercury (Hg)

0	13,630	140·3	0.0124×10^{-5}	8·21	430×10^{-8}	0·0288	1.82×10^{-4}
20	13,580	139·4	0·0114	8·69	461	0·0249	
50	13,510	138·6	0·0104	9·40	502	0·0207	
100	13,390	137·3	0·00928	10·5	571	0·0162	
150	13,260	136·5	0·00853	11·5	635	0·0134	
200	13,150	136·1	0·00802	12·3	691	0·0116	
250	13,030	135·7	0·00764	13·1	740	0·0103	
316	12,850	134·0	0·00673	14·0	815	0·0083	

Adapted from Table A–3, E. R. G. Eckert and R. M. Drake, Jr., *Heat and Mass Transfer*, McGraw-Hill Book Company, Inc., New York (1959).

Table A.5 Thermal Properties of Gases at Atmospheric Pressure

T (°K)	ρ (kg/m³)	c_p (J/kg deg C)	ν (m²/s)	k (W/m deg C)	α (m²/s)	μ (N s/m²)	Pr
				Air			
250	1·413	1005	$0·949 \times 10^{-5}$	0·0223	$1·32 \times 10^{-5}$	$1·60 \times 10^{-5}$	0·722
300	1·177	1006	1·57	0·0262	2·22	1·85	0·708
350	0·998	1009	2·08	0·0300	2·98	2·08	0·697
400	0·883	1014	2·59	0·0337	3·76	2·29	0·689
450	0·783	1021	2·89	0·0371	4·22	2·48	0·683
500	0·705	1030	3·79	0·0404	5·57	2·67	0·680
550	0·642	1039	4·43	0·0436	6·53	2·85	0·680
600	0·588	1055	5·13	0·0466	7·51	3·02	0·680
650	0·543	1063	5·85	0·0495	8·58	3·18	0·682
700	0·503	1075	6·63	0·0523	9·67	3·33	0·684
750	0·471	1086	7·39	0·0551	10·8	3·48	0·686
800	0·441	1098	8·23	0·0578	12·0	3·63	0·689
850	0·415	1110	9·07	0·0603	13·1	3·77	0·692
900	0·392	1121	9·93	0·0628	14·3	3·90	0·696
950	0·372	1132	10·8	0·0653	15·5	4·02	0·699
1000	0·352	1142	11·8	0·0675	16·8	4·15	0·702
1100	0·320	1161	13·7	0·0723	19·5	4·40	0·706
1200	0·295	1179	15·7	0·0763	22·0	4·63	0·714
1300	0·271	1197	17·9	0·0803	24·8	4·85	0·722

Hydrogen

250	0·0981	14,060	8·06 × 10⁻⁵	0·156	11·3 × 10⁻⁵	7·92 × 10⁻⁶	0·713
300	0·0819	14,320	10·9	0·182	15·5	8·96	0·706
350	0·0702	14,440	14·2	0·206	20·3	9·95	0·697
400	0·0614	14,490	17·7	0·229	25·7	10·9	0·690
450	0·0546	14,500	21·6	0·251	31·6	11·8	0·682
500	0·0492	14,510	25·7	0·272	38·2	12·6	0·675
550	0·0447	14,330	30·2	0·293	45·2	13·5	0·668
600	0·0408	14,540	35·0	0·315	53·1	14·3	0·664
650	0·0349	14,570	45·5	0·351	69·0	15·9	0·659
700	0·0306	14,680	56·9	0·384	85·6	17·4	0·664
750	0·0272	14,820	69·0	0·412	102	18·8	0·676
800	0·0245	14,970	82·2	0·440	120	20·2	0·686
850	0·0223	15,170	96·5	0·464	137	21·5	0·703

Oxygen

200	1·956	913·1	0·795 × 10⁻⁵	0·0182	1·02 × 10⁻⁵	14·9 × 10⁻⁶	0·745
250	1·562	915·6	1·144	0·0226	1·58	17·9	0·725
300	1·301	920·3	1·586	0·0267	2·24	20·6	0·709
350	1·113	929·0	2·080	0·0307	2·97	23·2	0·702
400	0·976	942·0	2·618	0·0346	3·77	25·5	0·695
450	0·868	956·7	3·199	0·0383	4·61	27·8	0·694
500	0·780	972·2	3·834	0·0417	5·50	29·9	0·697
550	0·710	988·1	4·505	0·0452	6·44	32·0	0·700
600	0·650	1004	5·214	0·0483	7·40	33·9	0·704

Table A.5. *Continued*

T (°K)	ρ (kg/m³)	c_p (J/kg deg C)	ν (m²/s)	k (W/m deg C)	α (m²/s)	μ (Ns/m²)	Pr
Nitrogen							
200	1·711	1043	$0·757 \times 10^{-5}$	0·0182	$1·02 \times 10^{-5}$	$12·9 \times 10^{-6}$	0·747
300	1·142	1041	1·563	0·0262	2·21	17·8	0·713
400	0·854	1046	2·574	0·0333	3·74	22·0	0·691
500	0·682	1056	3·766	0·0398	5·53	25·7	0·684
600	0·569	1076	5·119	0·0458	7·49	29·1	0·686
700	0·493	1097	6·512	0·0512	9·47	32·1	0·691
800	0·428	1123	8·145	0·0561	11·7	34·8	0·700
900	0·380	1146	9·106	0·0607	13·9	37·5	0·711
1000	0·341	1168	11·72	0·0648	16·3	40·0	0·724
1100	0·311	1186	13·60	0·0685	18·6	42·3	0·736
1200	0·285	1204	15·61	0·0719	20·9	44·5	0·748
Carbon dioxide							
250	2·166	803·9	$0·581 \times 10^{-5}$	0·0129	$0·740 \times 10^{-5}$	$12·6 \times 10^{-6}$	0·793
300	1·797	870·9	0·832	0·0166	1·06	15·0	0·770
350	1·536	900·2	1·119	0·0205	1·48	17·2	0·755
400	1·342	942·0	1·439	0·0246	1·95	19·3	0·738
450	1·192	979·7	1·790	0·0290	2·48	21·3	0·721
500	1·073	1013	2·167	0·0335	3·08	23·3	0·702
550	0·974	1047	2·574	0·0382	3·75	25·1	0·685
600	0·894	1076	3·002	0·0431	4·48	26·8	0·668

Carbon monoxide

T	ρ	c_p	ν	k	α	μ	Pr
250	0·841	1043	1.128×10^{-5}	0·0214	1.51×10^{-5}	15.4×10^{-6}	0·750
300	1·139	1042	1·567	0·0253	2·13	17·8	0·737
350	0·974	1043	2·062	0·0288	2·84	20·1	0·728
400	0·854	1048	2·599	0·0323	3·61	22·2	0·722
450	0·762	1055	3·188	0·0436	4·44	24·2	0·718
500	0·682	1063	3·819	0·0386	5·33	26·1	0·718
550	0·620	1076	4·496	0·0416	6·24	27·9	0·721
600	0·568	1088	5·206	0·0445	7·19	29·6	0·724

Water vapour

T	ρ	c_p	ν	k	α	μ	Pr
380	0·586	2060	0.216×10^{-4}	0·0246	2.04×10^{-5}	12.7×10^{-6}	1·060
400	0·554	2014	0·242	0·0261	2·24	13·4	1·040
450	0·490	1980	0·311	0·0299	3·07	15·3	1·010
500	0·441	1985	0·386	0·0339	3·87	17·0	0·996
550	0·400	1997	0·470	0·0379	4·75	18·8	0·991
600	0·365	2026	0·566	0·0422	5·73	20·7	0·986
650	0·338	2056	0·664	0·0464	6·66	22·5	0·995
700	0·314	2085	0·772	0·0505	7·72	24·3	1·000
750	0·293	2119	0·888	0·0549	8·83	26·0	1·005
800	0·274	2152	1·020	0·0592	10·0	27·9	1·010
850	0·258	2186	1·152	0·0637	11·3	29·7	1·019

Adapted from Table A–4, E. R. G. Eckert and R. M. Drake, Jr., *Heat and Mass Transfer*, McGraw-Hill Book Company, Inc., New York (1959). (*Note*: At pressures other than atmospheric, the density can be determined from the ideal gas equation, $\rho = p/RT$. Hence at any given temperature $\rho = \rho_0(p/p_0)$ where p_0 is atmospheric pressure and ρ_0 is given in the table. k, μ, and c_p may be assumed independent of pressure. ν and α are inversely proportional to the density; hence at a given temperature are inversely proportional to the pressure.)

Table A.6.   Normal Total Emissivity of Various Surfaces

	Ref.	t (°C)	Emissivity
Aluminium:			
Highly polished plate, 98·3% pure	11	237–576	0·039–0·057
Rough polish	1	100	0·18
Commercial sheet	1	100	0·09
Heavily oxidized	2	93–505	0·20–0·31
Al-surfaced roofing	5	38	0·216
Brass:			
Highly polished, 73·2 Cu, 26·7 Zn	11	247–357	0·028–0·031
Polished	1	100	0·06
Rolled plate, natural surface	10	22	0·06
Chromium, polished	1	100	0·075
Copper:			
Carefully polished electrolytic copper	6	80	0·018
Polished	1	100	0·052
Molten	3	1076–1278	0·16–0·13
Iron and steel:			
Steel, polished	1	100	0·066
Iron, polished	12	427–1028	0·14–0·38
Cast iron, polished	9	200	0·21
Cast iron, newly turned	10	22	0·44
Wrought iron, highly polished	16	38–249	0·28
Iron plate, completely rusted	10	19	0·69
Sheet steel, shiny oxide layer	10	24	0·82
Steel plate, rough	5	38–372	0·94–0·97
Cast iron, molten	15	1300–1400	0·29
Steel, molten	7	1522–1650	0·43–0·40
Stainless steel, polished	1	100	0·074
Lead, grey oxidized	10	24	0·28
Magnesium oxide	8	278–827	0·55–0·20
Nichrome wire, bright	14	49–1000	0·65–0·79
Nickel-silver, polished	1	100	0·135
Platinum filament	4	27–1230	0·036–0·192
Silver, polished, pure	11	227–627	0·02–0·032
Tin, bright tinned iron	10	23	0·043, 0·064
Tungsten filament	18	3320	0·39
Zinc, galvanized sheet iron, fairly bright	10	28	0·23

Table A.6. *Continued*

	Ref.	t (°C)	Emissivity
Asbestos board	10	23	0·96
Brick:			
Red, rough	10	21	0·93
Building	14	1000	0·45
Fireclay	14	1000	0·75
Magnesite, refractory	14	1000	0·38
Candle soot	17	97–272	0·952
Lampblack, other blacks	14	50–1000	0·96
Graphite, pressed, filed surface	8	249–516	0·98
Concrete tiles	14	1000	0·63
Enamel, white fused, on iron	10	19	0·90
Glass, smooth	10	22	0·94
Oak, planed	10	21	0·90
Flat black lacquer	5	38–94	0·96–0·98
Oil paints, 16 different, all colours	13	100	0·92–0·96
Aluminium paints, various	13	100	0·27–0·67
Radiator paint, bronze	1	100	0·51
Paper, thin, pasted on blackened plate	10	19	0·92, 0·94
Plaster, rough lime	16	10–87	0·91
Roofing paper	10	21	0·91
Water (calculated from spectral data)		0–100	0·95–0·963

(*Note:* When temperatures and emissivities appear in pairs separated by dashes, they correspond; and linear interpolation is permissible.)
By courtesy of H. C. Hottel, from *Heat Transmission*, 3rd ed., by W. H. McAdams, McGraw-Hill Book Company, Inc., New York (1954).

REFERENCES

1. Barnes, B. T., Forsythe, W. E., and Adams, E. Q. *J. Opt. Soc. Amer.*, Vol. 37, 804 (1947).
2. Binkley, E. R., private communication (1933).
3. Burgess, G. K. *Natl. Bur. Stand.*, Bull. 6, Sci. paper 121, 111 (1909).
4. Davisson, C., and Weeks, J. R. Jr. *J. Opt. Soc. Amer.*, Vol. 8, 581 (1924).
5. Heilman, R. H. *Trans. ASME*, FSP 51, 287 (1929).
6. Hoffman, K. Z. *Physik*, Vol. 14, 310 (1923).
7. Knowles, D., and Sarjant, R. J. *J. Iron and Steel Inst.* (London), Vol. 155, 577 (1947).
8. Pirani, M. *J. Sci. Instrum.*, Vol. 16, 12 (1939).
9. Randolf, C. F., and Overhaltzer, M. *J. Phys. Rev.*, Vol. 2, 144 (1913).
10. Schmidt, E. *Gesundh-Ing.*, Beiheft 20, Reihe 1, 1–23 (1927).

11. Schmidt, H., and Furthman, E. *Mitt. Kaiser-Wilhelm-Inst. Eisenforsch. Dusseldorf, Abhandle.*, Vol. 109, 225 (1928).
12. Snell, F. D. *Ind. Eng. Chem.*, Vol. 29, 89 (1937).
13. Standard Oil Development Company, personal communication (1928).
14. Thring, M. W. *The Science of Flames and Furnaces*, Chapman and Hall, London (1952).
15. Thwing, C. B. *Phys. Rev.*, Vol. 26, 190 (1908).
16. Wamsler, F. *Z. Ver. deut. Ing.*, Vol. 55, 599 (1911); *Mitt. Forsch.*, Vol. 98, 1 (1911).
17. Wenzl, M., and Morawe, F. *Stahl u. Eisen*, Vol. 47, 867 (1927).
18. Zwikker, C. *Arch. néerland. sci.*, Vol. 9, 207 (1925).

Table A.7.   Diffusion Coefficients

Water in air : $D \, (\text{ft}^2/\text{h}) = 0.892 \dfrac{p_0}{p} \left(\dfrac{T}{T_0} \right)^{1.81}$

$p_0 = 14.22 \, \text{lbf/in}^2 \, ; \quad T_0 = 460°\text{R}$

Diffusing material	Medium of diffusion	Temperature (°C)	Diffusion coefficient (m^2/s)	Schmidt number (v/D)
NH_3	Air	0	0.216×10^{-4}	0.634
CO_2	Air	0	0.120	1.14
CO_2	H_2	18	0.605	0.158
Hg	N_2	19	32.515	0.00424
O_2	Air	0	0.153	0.895
O_2	N_2	12	0.203	0.681
H_2	Air	0	0.547	0.250
H_2	O_2	14	0.775	0.182
H_2	N_2	12.5	0.738	0.187
H_2O	Air	8	0.206	0.615
H_2O	Air	16	0.281	0.488
C_6H_6	Air	0	0.075	1.83
C_6H_6	CO_2	0	0.053	1.37
C_6H_6	H_2	0	0.294	3.26
CS_2	Air	20	0.088	1.68
Ether	Air	20	0.077	1.93
Ethyl alcohol	Air	0	0.101	1.36
Ethyl alcohol	Air	40	0.118	1.45

Adapted from Table A–9, E. R. G. Eckert and R. M. Drake, Jr., *Heat and Mass Transfer*, McGraw-Hill Book Company, Inc., New York (1959).

Index